ABOUT THE AUTHOR

J. Robert Oppenheimer has been director of the Institute for Advanced Study at Princeton, New Jersey, since 1947. He is a physicist trained at Harvard, Cambridge and Göttingen who was for eighteen years Professor of Physics at the University of California and the California Institute of Technology. Between 1943 and 1945 he was director of the laboratory at Los Alamos in New Mexico, where the first atomic bombs were made. From 1945 through 1953 he served in many advisory positions to the Atomi [illegible] the White House, and the Department [illegible] in the spring of 1954, in a much pu [illegible] was denied security clearance. He is t [illegible] *the Common Understanding*, published [illegible] in 1954.

The Open Mind

by

J. ROBERT OPPENHEIMER

Simon and Schuster • New York

1955

PUBLISHED BY SIMON AND SCHUSTER, INC.
ROCKEFELLER CENTER, 630 FIFTH AVENUE
NEW YORK 20, N. Y.

FIRST PRINTING

LIBRARY OF CONGRESS CATALOG CARD NUMBER: 55–10043
MANUFACTURED IN THE UNITED STATES OF AMERICA
BY H. WOLFF BOOK MFG. CO., INC., NEW YORK, N. Y.

CONTENTS

AUTHOR'S NOTE

THE CHAPTERS *of this book are eight lectures that I have given. Four of them deal with atomic weapons and some related questions of policy. The other four bear on the relationship between science as an intellectual activity and the wider culture of our times. The two sets of themes are distinct, but there are points at which they are relevant to each other. I have not included any papers on physics, either technical or popular, nor any papers devoted to the special questions of education and patronage in the sciences.*

Each lecture is accompanied by a brief statement of the circumstances of its delivery, and by its date. The dates are material, for the world has changed a great deal in the years during which these talks were given.

J. ROBERT OPPENHEIMER

AUGUST 1955

I

Atomic Explosives

THIS LECTURE *was delivered in Pittsburgh, Pennsylvania, before the George Westinghouse Centennial Forum on May 16, 1946.*

I

Atomic Explosives

THIS TALK is to be a brief report on the future of atomic explosives. It will have to be a very incomplete and a very one-sided talk; I can hope that you will agree with me that the part of the matter that I can discuss, if not the most entertaining, is at least the most important.

When I looked over my notes for this talk, I was reminded of a story, very old and not very funny, but relevant. There was a professor of zoology at the University of Munich, and he had the habit of asking candidates about worms, until it came to such a pass that candidates studied no other subject but worms. And then, one day, he flabbergasted his student and said, "Tell me about elephants," and the candidate said, "The elephant is a large animal. It has a wormlike trunk. Worms may be divided into the following classes . . ." My talk to you this afternoon will be along these lines.

I cannot tell you of the probable future technical developments of atomic explosives. When the war was over we recognized that we had only scratched the surface of this problem; and no doubt since then some further progress has been made, both in development and in understanding. But these are things that we cannot talk about here. When, if ever, they can be talked about openly, it will be a very different world, and to my way of thinking a very much better one.

As for the uses of atomic explosives, the one that has been most widely discussed, the one in which their pre-eminence was first established and is most obvious, is the strategic bombardment of cities. No doubt there can be important tactical applications as well. I have even heard some discussion of the possibility of using them against naval craft, but on these ignorance and inexperience, as well as the requirements of secrecy, keep me from talking. There has even been a little talk of possible beneficent applications of atomic explosives, such as the blasting of polar ice or the possible control of major natural phenomena such as tornadoes, earthquakes, eruptions. There is enough energy in atomic explosives to give these vague suggestions an air of plausibility; even the weapons so far used release an energy about one thousandth of that in the San Francisco earthquake. But of course the forces produced by an atomic explosion have a very different sort of order from those involved in the great natural phenomena of quakes and of tornadoes; and the radiation and radioactivities that accompany any major atomic explosion must at least complicate its application to benign purposes. If men are ever to speak of the benefits of atomic energy, I think these applications will at most play a very small part in what they have in mind.

There is only one future of atomic explosives that I can regard with any enthusiasm: that they should never be used in war. Since in any major total war, such as we have lived through in these late years, they will most certainly be used, there is nothing modest in this hope for the future: It is that there be no such wars again. I should like to speak today on some considerations bearing upon the realization of that hope. This is a subject that seems to me worthy of careful study, and of the best thought of our times.

Some months ago, I had the privilege of working with a group of consultants to the Secretary of State's Committee on Atomic Energy. We spent many weeks exploring this problem, which is commonly defined in a sort of code as "The International Control of Atomic Energy." This is a code because the real problem is the prevention of war. Since that time our conclusions, expurgated of all secret or classified matter, have been made public, and may in one way or another have come to your attention. They were made public in order to facilitate public understanding and discussion, a discussion made more necessary by the difficulty of the problem, made more difficult by the secrecy which has been maintained and is still maintained about many of its technical elements. What I should like to do today is to add a few comments which may help to supplement the report that was made public, and to make explicit some of the things left implicit in it, to restore a balance of emphasis which was partially lost, perhaps, in the accidents of its release.

The heart of our proposal was the recommendation of an International Atomic Development Authority, entrusted with the research, development, and exploitation of the peaceful applications of atomic energy, with the elimination from national armaments of atomic weapons, and with the studies and researches and controls that must be directed toward that end. In this proposal we attempted to meet, and to put into a constructive context, two sets of facts, both long recognized, and commonly regarded as contributing to the difficulty, if not to the insolubility, of the problem.

The first of these facts is that the science, the technology, the industrial development involved in the so-called beneficial uses of atomic energy appear to be inextricably intertwined with those involved in making atomic weapons. You will hear reports this afternoon on the so-called beneficial uses of atomic energy. They come to us not in the form of answers but in the form of questions, and that for two reasons: In the first place, one of these uses is for the development of power, and this is something that has not been effectively done. No one knows to what extent such power will be economically profitable; no one knows to what extent technical problems may delay or complicate the development of atomic power as power. We have here a beginning; but we don't have any answers. We don't have a tree with fruit ripe on it, for us to shake the fruit down. The other application is in essence to research; and it is in the nature of research that you pay your "two bits" first, that you go in and you don't know what you are going to see. Therefore, if I speak of "beneficial applications," I want to make it clear that I don't know at all precisely what they are, but I share the belief that is widespread in the American people that a development of this kind in the hands of intelligent and resourceful men will lead to good things. The beginnings of these things you will hear described today.

But one thing I must go into: The same raw material, uranium, is needed for the use of atomic energy for power as for atomic bombs. The plants of an atomic power program may not be ideally suited for the production of bomb materials, but in a pinch—and atomic warfare is a pinch—they can be made to do. The various fissionable materials derived from uranium and thorium that play such a decisive part in the power program, or even in the use of atomic energy for research reactors and for advancing science and medicine and the practical arts, are, or can with more or less effort, be made into atomic explosives. The same physics which must be learned and studied and extended in the one field will help with the other—although there are of course some things in the higher art of bomb-making that as yet appear to have no other application. It is true that the properties that make a fissionable material, that make it useful for reactors for power or for research, are not quite the same properties that make it useful for bombs. Natural uranium can be used in a power plant, but I don't think a bomb can be made of it. Uranium considerably enriched in the isotope 235 can be more flexibly, more effectively used in a reactor; but I am not sure that it can be made explosive, and am fairly confident that it would be so ineffective as not to warrant the effort. Even plutonium can be doctored—not without prohibitive cost if it is to be completely nonexplosive—but to be made a relatively very ineffective explosive, and a difficult one to use in the present state of the art. I don't need to tell you that the art may change, and that no kind of control is worth anything which doesn't make provision for such change. It's not only that it can; it probably will, in one way or another. These differences in the requirements for controlled and explosive uses of atomic energy, might, if appropriately recognized in law, keep a group of individuals from making atomic weapons out of the materials of peacetime industry; they could retard and thus perhaps discourage nations otherwise prevented from the exploitation of atomic energy; but this isn't the problem; for to any who are actively engaged in such exploitation they could provide a deterrent so slight as to constitute a most dangerous illusion. Thus a mere prohibition on the activities of nations in the field of atomic energy sufficiently incisive to inspire confidence that, if enforced, it would prevent rapid conversion to atomic armament, would at the same time close this field to the exploitation of any of its benefits. This fact, which further technical developments appear unlikely to invalidate, has long been regarded as an almost decisive difficulty on the path of international control. It might have appeared so to us, too, if there had not been a greater one. For even if the course of development of atomic energy for peace were entirely distinct from its development for war, even if it were universally agreed that there were no peaceful applications of atomic energy worthy of interest or of effort, we should still be faced with the fact that there exists in the world today no machinery for making effective a prohibition against the national development of atomic armaments. In the light of this fact, that to my mind touches upon the heart of the problem, the close technical parallelism and interrelation of the peaceful and the military applications of atomic energy ceases to be a difficulty, and becomes a help. This does not, unfortunately, mean that it guarantees a solution. But it does mean that it provides a basis for seeking a healthy solution that would not otherwise exist.

If there were nothing to do with atomic energy but make bombs, there might still, it is true, be a convention between nations not to do so. Such conventions have in the past seldom withstood the strain of rivalries between nations preparing for war, nor does it seem likely that they could do so in the future in the case of a weapon whose effectiveness, especially in surprise, is so spectacular. For this reason two proposals have long been current for supplementing international conventions with some form of international action. One of these would set up a scheme of multilateral or international inspection, whose sole function would be to attempt to establish that the conventions were in fact being observed. It is conceivable that if the conventions were sufficiently radical, comprising, for instance, the total renunciation of all mining and refining of uranium, such a procedure might work. But

I doubt this, even in that case. I doubt whether the agency entrusted with such inspection could even then have the motivation, or the personnel, or the skill, or the experience, or the knowledge, or the endurance to carry out such a dreary, sterile, and policeman-like job. I doubt whether the relations between this agency and the nations and nationals whom it was instructed to police would be such as to diminish the nationalism leading to war, or to inspire the confidence of the nations in each other, or to advance the cause of the unification of the world, or to serve as a useful prototype for the elimination of weapons of mass destruction, perhaps equally, perhaps even more terrible. Therefore one may perhaps not regret that the door to this sort of international action is largely closed by the impossibility of denying to the world in any long term an opportunity to explore the beneficial possibilities of atomic energy. For once such exploration is allowed to the nations, the technical complexities and human inadequacies of an international inspection scheme as a sole safeguard become manifestly insupportable.

The second suggestion for international action to supplement the renunciation by nations of atomic armaments has a more affirmative character. It is that an international agency be entrusted with the making and possession of atomic weapons. Though there has been much in this proposal that has seemed attractive, it has two weaknesses, and probably fatal ones: The more serious is that there is nothing that an international agency can do, or should do, with such weapons. They are not police weapons. They are singularly unsuited for distinguishing between innocent and guilty or for taking even crudely into account the distinction between the guilt of individuals and that of peoples; they are themselves a supreme expression in a weapon of the concepts of total war. The second difficulty, in some sense inescapable in any form of international action, but desperately acute in this, is that such stocks of atomic weapons, however earnestly they are proclaimed international, however ingeniously they are distributed on earth, would nonetheless offer the most terrible temptation to national seizure, for the almost immediate military advantage that their use might afford.

These two examples do give recognition to the need, in any system of outlawing atomic weapons, of international action. In this I think they are sound. In fact, in another context, the study—but not the production—of atomic weapons, and inspection to prevent the illegal mining of uranium, both would seem to be essential functions of an international authority.

It is time to turn to the second of the great difficulties that have from the outset been regarded as preventing any effective international control. We have already referred to it. It is the absence in the world today of any machinery adequate to provide such control, any precedent for such machinery, or even any adequate patterns of the past to provide such a precedent. Just this is the reason why the problem is so much of a challenge, why we may be sustained by the hope that its solution would provide such precedent, such patterns, for a wider application. It did not take atomic weapons to make wars, or to make wars terrible, or to make wars total. If there had never been and could never be an atomic bomb, the problem of preventing war in an age when science and technology have made it too destructive, and too terrible to endure, would still be with us. There would be the block-buster, the rocket, the V-2, the incendiary, the M-67, and their increase; there would no doubt be biological warfare. There would be, and there still are. But the atomic bomb, most spectacular of proven weapons, the most inextricably intertwined with constructive developments and the least fettered by private or by vested interest or by long national tradition is for these and other reasons the place to start. For in this field there is possible a system of control that is consistent with, that is based upon, the technical realities and with the human realities in the deep sense. In this field, there is a solution that can be made to work.

Many have said that without world government there could be no permanent peace, and without peace there would be atomic warfare. I think one must agree with this. Many have said that there could be no outlawry of weapons and no prevention of war unless international law could apply to the citizens of nations, as federal law does to citizens of states, or have made manifest the fact that international control is not compatible with absolute national sovereignty. I think one must agree with this. Many have said that atomic energy could not be controlled if the controlling authority could be halted by a veto, as in many actions can the Security Council of the United Nations. I think one must agree with this too. With those who argue that it would be desirable to have world government, an appropriate delegation of national sovereignty, laws applicable to individuals in all nations, it would seem most difficult to differ; but with those who argue that these things are directly possible, in their full and ultimately necessary scope, it may be rather difficult for me to agree.

What relation does the proposal of an International Atomic Development Authority, entrusted with a far-reaching monopoly of atomic energy—what relation does this proposal of ours have to do with these questions? It proposes that in the field of atomic energy there be set up a world government, that in this field there be renunciation of national sovereignty, that in this field there be no legal veto power, that in this field there be international law. How is this possible, in a world of sovereign nations? There are only two ways in which this ever can be possible: one is conquest, that destroys sovereignty; and the other is the partial renunciation of that sovereignty. What is here proposed is such a partial renunciation, sufficient, but not more than sufficient, for an Atomic Development Authority to come into being, to exercise its functions of development, exploitation and control, to enable it to live and grow and to protect the world against the use of atomic weapons and provide it with the benefits of atomic energy.

Whatever else happens, there is likely to be a discussion of the control of atomic energy in the United Nations Commission set up for that purpose, and not in the very distant future, I would say. Should these discussions eventuate in the proposal of an International Authority, and in a charter for that Authority, these proposals and that charter would in the end be presented for ratification to the several nations. Each nation, the small as well as the great, can exercise its sovereign right to refuse such ratification. Should that happen, there would be no Atomic Development Authority, and in my opinion probably no trustworthy, effective, international control of atomic energy. Should a nation, after the creation of the Authority, exercise its sovereign right and withdraw from it, or fail with regard to it to carry out the accepted and major conditions of the charter, then there will also be no Atomic Development Authority; unlike the Security Council, it presumably could not survive the application of the veto to its major provisions. But if it comes into existence, and insofar as it stays in existence, it will provide, in this field, the international sovereignty whose necessity has been so generally recognized.

Perhaps, one will say, no international enterprise can live under such conditions. But the conditions themselves will not remain unaffected by the enterprise. Its coming into existence will be a step that, once learned, can be repeated, a commitment that, once made in one field, can be extended to others. If this is to happen, the Development Authority will have to have a healthy life of its own; it will have to flourish, to be technically strong, to be useful to mankind, to have a staff and an organization and a way of life in which there is some pride, and some cause for pride. This would not be possible if there were nothing of value to do with atomic energy. This would not be possible if the prevention of atomic armament were its only concern, if all other activity was technically so separable and separate from atomic armament that it could remain in national hands. In the long struggle to find a way of reconciling national and international sovereignty, the peaceful applications of atomic energy can only be a help. It is perhaps doubtful that we should have had a federal government had not those functions which could not safely nor effectively be carried out by the states had a certain importance for the people of this country.

The Board of Consultants to the State Department was aware of the supreme necessity for providing the Authority with work that could attract men, and consolidate and inspire them. It was equally aware of the complementary dangers of a too complete, a too absolute monoply. These dangers are of two kinds: on the one hand, a monopoly which is not subject to criticism is likely to go to seed; it is likely not to be on its toes; it is likely in the end to become bureaucratically inbred. On the other hand, if you have no living, legitimate contact between the operations of an Authority like this, and the activities of scientists, engineers, and business men operating outside the Authority, in national or in private agencies, then you have no way of being sure that you are not missing many important bets. A too absolute monopoly would be dangerous both to the health of the monopoly and to the surveillance activities which an Authority of this kind must maintain.

For this reason we found it important to point out that there were many activities in the field of atomic energy which either in themselves or because they are easy and reliable to control and inspect and supervise, could not lend themselves to evasive or diversionary developments of atomic weapons. An example of this kind is the whole field of the use of tracers. An example of this kind is the use of reactors for research. An example of this kind which is somewhat more marginal, is the use of reactors which burn and do not produce explosive material for power, and in which the best steps you can take to complicate and delay the use of this material for explosives have been taken, so that it isn't a thing that can be done in an hour's effort or in a month's effort or by a few angry individuals. I think the importance of this point is this: there are safe activities which you can leave, for instance, in the hands of the government of the United States or the corporations of the United States or the universities of the United States. For this reason, there will be good, technical liaison between the Authority and these more private agencies. This will, on the one hand, tend to correct the bureaucracy that is implicit in monopoly. On the other hand, it will give the International Authority some method of remaining cognizant of the developments in the field which happen not to have been carried out by itself.

If any great note of confidence or gayety has invested these brief words, it would be a distortion of the spirit in which I should have wished to speak to you. No thoughtful man can look to the future with any complete assurance that the world will not again be ravaged by war, by a total war in which atomic weapons contribute their part to the ultimate wreck and attrition of this our Western civilization. My own view is that the development of these weapons can make, if wisely handled, the problem of preventing war, not more hopeless, but more hopeful, than it would otherwise have been, and that this is so not merely because it intensifies the urgency of our hopes, but because it provides new and healthy avenues of approach. In developing these avenues the fact that there is so far-reaching a technical inseparability of the constructive uses of atomic energy from the destructive ones—a fact that at first sight might appear to render the problem only more difficult—this fact is precisely the central vital element that can make effective action possible. If we are clear on this, we shall have some guide for the future.

II

Atomic Energy as a Contemporary Problem

THIS IS *a lecture given in Washington, D.C., to a group of officers in the armed services, the Foreign Service, and the State Department, on September 17, 1947.*

II

Atomic Energy as a Contemporary Problem

IN SPEAKING about a subject with a very pretentious title and speaking of some really almost trivial considerations, I cannot help being reminded of a story of long ago which comes to my mind whenever any general question of what to do about atomic energy is raised. I had a colleague at the University of California, Arthur Ryder. He was a lonely man, and he liked to take young children out and entertain them, and buy them ice cream. One day he took a little friend of mine out; and she appeared bored so he started to wiggle his ears for her. She looked at him and said, "Uncle Arthur, how do you do that?" He thought very hard, and after a pause he said, "It's very hard to describe. You just feel a general sense of strain."

This seems to be so much the spirit in which all atomic undertakings operate that I would like to say a few words about the reason for this sense of strain or—at least some of the reasons for the sense of strain. It would not be possible, and it would not be profitable, to discuss the technical aspects of atomic energy. Nor do I think the technical problems, however complex, are the reasons for the difficulties of policy decision in this field. They lie in the very objectives which must be concurrently pursued, and which to some extent contradict each other. We can come at that in two ways, and I will illustrate the two ways.

If we were to ask this group what is important, that we be strong in atomic energy—that we have security in the atomic age—two years from now or ten years from now or twenty years from now, you would answer yes. This is a very difficult answer on the basis of which to plan, because the requirements for security at these three different times are not identical, and it requires some ingenuity to find those elements in the problems of atomic energy which make it possible to reconcile them.

Looked at in a little deeper way, there are three planes on which we have more or less explicitly asserted that we would like to achieve security: One is international control; this is the official policy of the United States. It is a very far-reaching control which would eliminate the rivalry between nations in this field, which would prevent the surreptitious arming of one nation against another, which would provide some cushion of time before atomic attack, and presumably therefore before any attack with weapons of mass destruction, and which would go a long way toward removing atomic energy at least as a source of conflict between the powers. That kind of security is a kind which I think is nonobtainable by any other method. But as is clear to you, and as we shall have reason to discuss, the fact that this is the most desirable form of security does not also mean that it will be realized.

Second, there is the path of technical superiority, which has a dual purpose. By this superiority I mean that we should always be in the forefront as far as ideas, management and development are concerned—we should as much as possible avoid being taken by surprise as far as technical development goes, we should know our business and have an active and flourishing group of people working in the field of atomic energy. This has a dual function—on the one hand of giving us the opportunity of maintaining a freedom of maneuver in this field which we would entirely lose if we were outstripped or surprised by some foreign effort, and in the second place, it is regarded—and I think rightly regarded—as a strong deterrent to aggression against us.

The third plane is the plane of actual strength, which in this field—and this field is clearly not separate from others—has itself a number of elements which need to be spelled out. It means among other things effective, maximumly effective, defense against probable methods of delivery of atomic weapons, proper and necessary dispersion for survival in the event of attack, proper schemes for the necessary and probably extremely difficult effort of mobilization; it means having effective and ready means of retaliation; it means a detailed strategic co-ordination for the use of our atomic facilities.

The things you would do to achieve international control, to achieve a sort of long-term technical superiority, and that you would do to achieve a maximum actual relative strength, are not always consistent. And the problem arises of finding a balance that is at all times reasonable and does not sell out any one of these three objectives. This means you have to look at the detail of what the problems of atomic energy are, and see what features there are that lend themselves to achieving three things at once, or work toward three things at once, in a way which would not at first seem possible.

This isn't quite trivial. For instance, if our problem were the achievement of the greatest actual military strength two years from now, and there were no question at all of longer-term objectives, if there were no thought of ultimate international concord, and if there were no thought of the health and strength of our scientific and technical development twenty years from now, one would be inclined to follow a very close-in approach, in which a minimum number of people were involved in policy making, a minimum number of people were informed about the realities of atomic energy, in which minimum development was undertaken because development pays off slowly, in which the concentration was almost entirely on expanding and improving slightly the known methods of proceeding from raw materials to atomic weapons. Our goal would be a large stock, the largest possible stockpile, the minimum possible dissemination of information. This would be the short-term program.

Such a program would match one of the objectives. It would not match all three. You may think it strange that I have included the achievement of international control as one of the things to keep in mind in planning atomic activities. This I think—and you have heard it from Dr. Fox and from Mr. Osborn—is the only way in which this country can have a security comparable to that which it had in the years before the war. It is the only way in which we will be able to live with bad governments, with new discoveries, with irresponsible governments such as are likely to arise in the next hundred years, without living in fairly constant fear of the surprise use of these weapons, and their surprise development.

As you also know, the whole notion of international control, when you examine it with some care, comes down to that of an international co-operative development; even the experiences within the United Nations are revealing in this respect. On the one hand, the representatives of the nine other non-Soviet states who sit in the United Nations Commission have, it seems to me, become convinced of the fundamental soundness of the United States proposals. They were not all so convinced initially, and I do not believe their acquiescence is in most cases simply a result of a desire to conform to the United States position. I think it results from conviction. The vitality of the fundamental ideas of the United States position is attested, I think, by its acceptance.

At the same time, I think no one can take with any seriousness the hope or expectation that the Soviet Union will accede, or that it will come closer to acceding, to what is now the majority plan. That is not too hard to understand. The cornerstone of our proposal is an institution which requires candidness and great openness in regard to technical realities and policy. It involves the working co-operation between peoples, irrespective of nationality. It involves a maximum effort to abolish national rivalries in the field of atomic energy, and in all dangerous areas of atomic energy it involves a total and genuine international action. It is clear that, even for the United States, proposals of this kind involve a very real renunciation. Among other things they involve a more or less permanent renunciation of any hope that the United States might live in relative isolation from the rest of the world. I think I am giving away no improper confidences in saying that many representatives of other powers were genuinely goggle-eyed when they found out what our proposals were, and that we meant them. Initially they thought they were radical to a point and hard to justify. But if for the United States and the western European powers some sacrifices are required by these proposals, the sacrifices, the renunciation, required of Russia are of another order of magnitude. That is because the proposed pattern of control stands in a very gross conflict to the present patterns of state power in Russia. The ideological underpinning of that power, namely the belief in the inevitability of conflict between Russia and the capitalist world, would be repudiated by a co-operation as intense or as intimate as is required by our proposals for the control of atomic energy. Thus what we have asked of the Russians is a very far-reaching renunciation and reversal of the basis of their state power, and of their state power itself. It does not seem to me likely that we have found inducements, or cajolery, or threats which together are adequate to make them take this great plunge. That does not mean, I suppose, that this will never happen, but it will almost certainly not happen as a result of the discussions in the United Nations.

The whole notion of international control presupposes a certain confidence, a confidence which may be not inconsistent with carrying a gun when you sit down to play poker, but at least is consistent with sitting down to play poker. In the year and a half since the effort on these problems started we have found ourselves forced by the Soviet moves, and by the changing political situation throughout the world, over and over again to take steps which were in essence a repudiation of that confidence; and the Soviet has taken even more grave steps in repudiation of that confidence. The whole plane on which agreement—and agreement is not enough—could be negotiated has disappeared; and beyond agreement there are the incredibly much more difficult problems of implementing the plan and giving life to the plan.

I therefore think that to believe seriously today that in six months, a year, or a year and a half, we will have something resembling an Atomic Development Authority, the cooperative development of atomic energy, involves a kind of schizophrenia which can only lead to very bad political confusion. I even think the worry—"What would happen if the Russians suddenly reversed their stand, embraced our proposals and started to work to put them in effect?"—is an empty worry. It is in the nature of the proposals we have made—a protection afforded by our plans for the United States—that they cannot be implemented in very bad faith, that they presuppose a very large measure of peaceful intention, of co-operation, of confidence and candor before they can get started.

But before concluding this consideration it is necessary to say that a number of people of thoughtful character and undoubted devotion to this problem are somewhat less certain that we should not settle for less, that in these negotiations we have set our sights far too high. We have asked for things that cannot be realized; and in view of the privileged position of a police state in the possession of weapons of this kind, we might do well to make a cheaper bargain. I have had many discussions with Dr. Conant about this. I know he is going to talk to you next week; and I believe he will speak about this question. He has some suggestions, which he thinks have not been taken seriously enough, and which come down to a much more modest proposal for internationalization, based essentially on leaving nuclear fuel in the ground, and cutting back the scale of technical activity to a point where very much less interference with sovereignty, and thus very much less international co-operation, would be involved. I myself am confident—I am most reluctantly confident—that the arguments that were given in the Acheson-Lilienthal report are correct arguments, and that such cheap solutions do not exist. But this is a possibility which should not be casually dismissed.

Under these circumstances it would seem rational to me to expect, in the immediate or in the foreseeable future, as a result of what goes on in the United Nations or, for that matter, in any bilateral or multilateral negotiations that might be entered into to supplement the work of the United Nations, that neither agreement nor the fruit of agreement actually will eventuate in the setting up of international co-operative control and development. I don't think anyone knows either a short means of achieving this, or of a sure means of achieving it. Yet it would almost certainly not be right, looking ahead for a period of time, to write off the possibility of this sort of development for good, because it has in it, as the original arguments that moved the government of this country to propose such control clearly showed, the seeds of a kind of security which is not obtainable in any other way, and which we would want even if there did not exist the government of the Soviet Union, which we would want if political arrangements of the world were very different from what they are today. Some day we will want to come back to this. And this means that in our own operations, in the way we deal with atomic energy and its related problems in this country, in the way in which we deal with the western European countries, one of the conditions, not an overriding condition, but one of the conditions that needs to be kept in mind is that we conform to those plans which would make it most likely that in the long term the problem of atomic energy could not merely be borne with but could be solved, and that means internationalization.

What does this mean in concrete terms? I don't think I

can answer that except with a few simple points by way of illustration. The first is, as I have said before, that we want to keep the initiative, and that means that we do not want to find ourselves in a situation in which we are concentrating on problems as they appeared at the end of 1945, when in other lines, and with other scientific impetus, and other scientific fortifications there are perhaps new developments which make fundamentally obsolete all that we are doing. We don't want to be caught in a bad position. This is a leadership in ideas and in men; and of course it involves a maximum acquaintance with the work that is going on abroad.

Even in these postwar years where the pattern of civilized life in Europe has been worn so very thin, of the two or three important experimental discoveries of the last two years, two at least come from Europe. One was carried out long before its publication in the cellar of an old house in Rome by three Italians who were under sentence of death from the Germans, because they belonged to the Italian Resistance. They were rescued by the uncle of one of the men from a labor squad at Cassino, and smuggled into a cellar in Rome. They got bored there, and they started to do experiments. These experiments were published last spring; and in the field of fundamental physics they created a real revolution in our thinking.

The other experiments were carried out under very much less dramatic circumstances, but with very modest equipment, by Powell and Occhialini, in England. I mention this only to say that under conditions where one would think that technical work abroad would be greatly handicapped, and we in this country would have all the advantages, this would be an oversimplified view of what is really taking place. Of course, these experiments have nothing whatever to do with atomic energy. These are fundamental things which at some time may conceivably have something to do with atomic energy, but they do not today, and probably never will.

As an important point, because of the whole pattern of our proposed plan of control, and because of the intimate mixture of constructive and destructive, of explosive and of power applications, of atomic energy, it is clear that quite apart from their usefulness in our own economy, in our own science, the long-term search for an international solution puts a very considerable value on developing the constructive applications of atomic energy.

Third, there is the question, to which I have to return over and over again, of the proper balance between openness and security, and the necessity, if one is to look to a heroic future in this field, for cultivating and for training young men, for cultivating a corps of people who are informed and knowledgeable and useful, for establishing appropriate relations with the scientists and technical people of other countries. There is also a manifest inadequacy in a total and uncompromising policy of security—a policy which this country has never adopted from the earliest days—to laying the foundation for any future possible internationalization.

There are other things as well, but they add up to the fact that if there is to be a solution along the lines of the United States proposals, not this year, not next year, but at some time in the future, then this area of work, in atomic energy, and its closely related fields, must be kept an area of scientific and rational co-operative activity, and must not be sewed up so tightly that it is not a part of the living culture and development of the country. This means in turn that one will have to adopt, for this reason as well as others, a somewhat dynamic approach to security. It means, for instance, that the policy of sitting tight on our knowledge and on our stockpiles would neither be of use to keeping open the door to later internationalization, nor be an effective course for maintaining our technical superiority.

In this field I can think of an analogy. There are examinations which are given with open books, because all the answers are not to be found in books. The field of atomic energy is an open-book examination. It is something where you can't look up the answers, and where your real assets are assets of capability, understanding, knowledge and competence.

This brings me to another point. If you talk about pre-eminence in atomic energy, there are two separate and not at first quite reconcilable views of what pre-eminence means. For one thing, if you compare what this country is doing with what is going on in England, which is spending ten per cent of what we are, or in France, which is spending one per cent of what we are, or in Russia, which is spending we don't know how much, if you compare thus, we would perhaps be markedly ahead; and that is a pre-eminence which we should never willingly sacrifice. There is another pre-eminence which comes from comparing what we were doing in 1945 with what we were doing in 1946 and what we were doing in 1945 with what we will be doing in 1950, from a sense of progress. The activities in this field won't survive if they compare favorably only with the activities elsewhere, and not favorably with the past activities in this country. There must be a sense of progress and achievement to give dynamic stability to an undertaking of this magnitude.

All this would be inadequate without one other consideration. At the present time, and I think in the foreseeable future, it will not be possible to arm atomically very quickly. The processes of accumulating fissionable material do not appear to lend themselves very well to the kind of speed-up which turned out to be so successful before the last war. There are two points there: One is a sense of the accelerating time schedule, which means that we could not afford so long a period of conversion from peace to armament; and the second is in the nature of the processes of production of fissionable material, which probably, if concentrated, let us say, into a year to give what we may conceive to be an adequate stockpile, would put unbearable strains on certain elements of our economy. Specifically, I don't think we could spare the power to create a stockpile of this kind in such a short time.

That is an argument which indicates that one cannot neglect the very short term, the actual status of available armament; but at the same time one cannot sit on it, however adequate, with any total assurance of superiority in this field. One has to find a balance; and in essence this is the same balance—the challenge with which this country will be faced in all other activities, during the coming years—the balance between freedom on the one hand and security on the other, between a dynamic and a static security.

I have made all this by way of preamble in order to take up four or five examples of issues where one might be tempted at first sight to give a quick solution, and where a consideration of the three planes on which we need to aim for security shows that no cheap solution is possible, and that on the contrary a certain subtlety of approach is required. The first has to do with our relations with other countries in this field. You may ask what there is that we want from the other countries. What is there that we want? It goes without saying that we have an interest in raw materials; but to be a little more general, we want the advantage of their brains and their work. Western Europe, as I have said, and Japan, for that matter—these are places where scientific work of extremely high quality is going on, and where it ought to continue to go on. We want their good will and we want their sympathy. We want the intellectuals of Europe to be friends of the United States and not enemies. These are some of the obvious things.

This which I have said of foreign scientists holds true of the nonproject scientists in this country. No atomic energy authority, no commission, could ever hope, or find it legitimate, to have most of the scientists of the country working on atomic energy. That would be completely out of focus. Ten per cent would be a large number, and that only in the fields most closely involved. I doubt if you could employ ten per cent of the chemists of the country on atomic energy. But we could get a great deal from the scientific and technical and industrial strength of those who are not full-time on atomic energy. It is a very great disadvantage to have to hire a man and tell him what he needs to know to do the job, and then see if he has any ideas. In order to progress in technical things there must be a fairly free dissemination of information; on the basis of this people who are not now professionally concerned will start thinking about a problem and they will have some sort of suggestion. They may write a paper about it, or start to make an experiment. This ability to draw on the nonco-ordinated resources of this country and of Europe is clearly something which we can enjoy to the extent to which we can make the realities of atomic energy known to people who are not working for the United States authority, the Atomic Energy Commission, as it is today. This is an extremely strong argument for examining with great care how great the area of openness can be, that it may not be merely a piece of technical information but an area of technical understanding. We must ask what benefit is such openness likely to be to a competing effort, and what usefulness may come to us from having a set of problems known far more widely.

There is a very good example in recent history of an action of which I most thoroughly approve, and which is the beginning of an attempt to make available to wider circles some of the instrumentalities and some of the information of atomic energy, and that lies in the field of isotope distribution. One might say offhand that in our relations with nonproject work in this country, and in our relations with other countries, at least friendly countries of western Europe, we might be guided by the principle that all those activities which would be delineated as "safe" in the field of atomic energy, which do not provide a physical basis for atomic armament, might well be shared. This would include a very great many things. It includes small reactors. It includes isotopes, going far beyond the list that was drawn up for distribution abroad.

Take the isotopes as an example. The distribution of isotopes, all of which can be produced by other methods, and which are primarily chosen for their value in biological research, is an extremely prudent step. These are being made available for our own benefit, for the good will involved, for the knowledge we hope to obtain, and because this is a decent, consistent gesture, painting some slight stroke in the picture of the world as we would like to see it in the future. This is an extremely prudent step in this picture. There will have to be others. But there are in this case also no blanket rules.

Another example—and I am largely discussing here things which always keep turning up about technical problems and are referred to the Advisory Committee of the Atomic Energy Commission—is the apparent conflict between the general support of science, and the pursuit of the immediate aims of technical jobs for atomic energy. Most scientists who work in universities work on things of rather abstract and long-range nature, and if you, let us say, do so harmless a thing as provide grants and fellowships for doctorate and post-doctorate studies, if you provide funds for the instruments and equipment, as the Office of Naval Research has done so well, you automatically provide an incentive to people to stay in the university laboratories and stay there longer than they might otherwise do. In this way you cut down at a time of extremely critical shortage of personnel the number of people who may work on the pressing, and sometimes horribly pressing, problems of establishing and maintaining atomic armament. Nevertheless, here again it would be a mistake to give a blanket answer. It is probably not within the power of all the agencies of the government of the United States combined to draw off into atomic energy activities very many more people than are now there working. But if that were done at the expense either of the training of young men, or the development of new knowledge in fundamental sciences, it would be an extremely costly bargain, increasing our temporary strength and involving a great price for the future.

There is then another area in which problems of this kind arise. To keep completely secret the design of the Hanford piles I think has never been a controversial thing. To keep secret the fact that we don't know how to do some things may be controversial because it may be that we really need some ideas, and the classification, or keeping secret, our ignorance of an area in which we haven't been able to make any progress may in some cases be a very serious hindrance to getting the insight, the bright ideas and the progress which would come if a much wider group of people could be interested. There are a considerable number of cases of this kind, ranging all the way from problems of weapons to problems of raw materials, where I myself have the feeling that what we are keeping secret are some ideas that aren't right, and what we need is to invite, by defining the problem, some new ideas that are. But clearly in all such cases an extremely close attention needs to be given to whether the revelation that we have not solved a problem may be a breach of military security or a source of comfort to a rival nation.

An area even more troublesome is this: The making of nuclear fuel, apart from the making of weapons, and a good deal of the operations having to do with the discovery and the processing of raw materials, are in many ways normal industrial operations. And everyone knows that an avid and eager participation on the part of industry in these programs would give us a strength, a fertility and an over-all competence which cannot be obtained if industries are merely assigned certain jobs. But in turn this costs something, because it is not reasonable to expect an industry to take an interest in a problem of this kind, unless it can see that it can make contributions which may turn out, may conceivably turn out, to be very profitable. It is not reasonable to ask an industry to participate unless it is likely to develop within its own staff the competent men, the knowledge, and the policy-making functions which it normally enjoys in its day-to-day operations in other fields. So if you try to use industry entirely as an instrument for carrying out the needed programs, for getting new plants built, for getting atomic armaments increased in the next year or two, you will dry up the interest that industry might have in a longer term. If you allow the industrial pattern to prevail entirely, that means that you will for a long time be doing nothing but building up very large and qualified staffs in the various industries, which won't pay off for many, many years to come. Clearly here again a compromise is required if the varied needs of our security are to be understood.

This has a more general application. In order to work well, people need to have some sense of participation in policy making; in order to make policy they have to know things, and in order to know things you have to tell them, you have to let them learn. The open approach to atomic energy which we would follow ideally if we had no worry that there were a competitor anywhere in the world, this open approach has the advantage that policy by and large will get made by the people who have the best brains, and who work hardest, whether it is in the laboratory, in the management of an industry, or in the government of the United States. This cannot be realized; but the advantages of not keeping technical knowledge and technical problems too highly compartmentalized lies in assuring that the policy-making fertility of the country will be involved. When I speak of policy, I don't of course mean only the highest political policy, but rather the question of what you do next, what kind of reactors you build, whether you pursue high-temperature reactors, which would be of interest for aircraft propulsion, whether you pursue power on a smaller or a larger scale, whether you use enriched fuel—these are typical of questions which are policy questions, which no centralized agency will in the long term be competent to answer, whose answers must emerge from a cognizant and responsible body of technical men.

I think there is another related area, and here I am speaking about matters of which I know even less. It seems to me that, both from the point of view of having an effective force for retaliation, and from the point of view of proper co-ordination of our more specifically defensive activities, quite a few people in military circles need to know what atomic energy is all about. They need to know the facts of this field, and typically they need to know the most highly classified facts. It seems to me here again that there is a conflict between drawing into the efforts the talent which is needed to make a strong and reasonably long-term program, and the precautions of security which would give us the greatest relative advantage if we felt that only the next year or two years or three years were of any consequence.

I have tried to spell out some of these questions because I believe that they are typical of the reason why atomic energy is not a trivial subject, even at this time, and why preoccupations ranging from the elementary one, how many bombs will we have next year, to the remote one, will we so conduct our affairs that we will have the power, the insight, the wisdom and the discipline to order the atomic energy activities of the world as a whole, whenever and as soon as the opportunity arises, need to be kept simultaneously in mind. I think there is a very high price to only short-term security, which none of us will be willing to pay. To those who would say that this is no time to be thinking of long-term things, or that it is sheer madness, with the "world as it is" to dream about international control, or again to those others who say that there is no security except in international control and that any other precautions are useless, I would quite profoundly disagree; to them I should like to tell a final story. It is a story of Confucius.

One day in a clearing in the forest, Confucius came upon a woman in deep mourning, wracked by sorrow. He learned that her son had just been eaten by a tiger; and he attempted to console her, to make clear how unavailing her tears would be, to restore her composure. He left, but had barely re-entered the forest, when the renewed sounds of weeping recalled him. "That is not all," the woman said. "You see, my husband was eaten here a year ago by this same tiger." Again Confucius attempted to console her and again he left only to hear renewed weeping. "Is that not all?" "Oh, no," she said. "The year before that my father too was eaten by the tiger." Confucius thought for a moment, and then said: "This would not seem to be a very salutary neighborhood. Why don't you leave it?" The woman wrung her hands. "I know," she said, "I know; but, you see, the government is so excellent."

III

The Open Mind

THIS TALK *was made on December 11, 1948, before a joint session of the Rochester Association for the United Nations and the Rochester Foreign Policy Association.*

III

The Open Mind

A FEW WEEKS ago the president of a college in the prairie states came to see me. Clearly, when he tried to look into the future, he did not like what he saw: the grim prospects for the maintenance of peace, for the preservation of freedom, for the flourishing and growth of the humane values of our civilization. He seemed to have in mind that it might be well for people, even in his small college, to try to take some part in turning these prospects to a happier end; but what he said came as rather a shock. He said, "I wonder if you can help me. I have a very peculiar problem. You see, out there, most of the students, and the teachers too, come from the farm. They are used to planting seed, and then waiting for it to grow, and then harvesting it. They believe in time and in nature. It is rather hard to get them to take things into their own hands." Perhaps, as much as anything, my theme tonight will have to do with enlisting time and nature in the conduct of our international affairs: in the quest for peace and a freer world. This is not meant mystically, for the nature which we must enlist is that of man; and if there is hope in it, that lies not least in man's reason. What elements are there in the conduct of foreign affairs which may be conducive to the exercise of that reason, which may provide a climate for the growth of new experience, new insight and new understanding? How can we recognize such growth, and be sensitive to its hopeful meaning, while there is yet time, through action based on understanding, to direct the outcome?

To such difficult questions one speaks not at all, or very modestly and incompletely. If there are indeed answers to be found, they will be found through many diverse avenues of approach—in the European Recovery Program, in our direct relations with the Soviet states, in the very mechanisms by which our policies are developed and determined. Yet you will not find it inappropriate that we fix attention on one relatively isolated, yet not atypical, area of foreign affairs—on atomic energy. It is an area in which the primary intent of our policy has been totally frustrated. It is an area in which it is commonly recognized that the prospects for success with regard to this primary intent are both dim and remote. It is an area in which it is equally recognized that this failure will force upon us a course of action in some important respects inconsistent with our original purposes. It is an area in which the excellence of our proposals, and a record in which we may and do take pride, have nevertheless not managed quite to quiet the uneasy conscience, nor to close the mind to further trouble.

The history of our policy and our efforts toward international atomic control is public; far more important, it has from the first aroused widespread interest, criticism and understanding, and has been the subject of debates in the Congress and the press, and among our people. There may even be some notion of how, if we had the last years to live over again, we might alter our course in the light of what we have learned, and some rough agreement as to the limits within which alternative courses of action, if adopted at a time when they were still open to us, could have altered the outcome. The past is in one respect a misleading guide to the future: It is far less perplexing.

Certainly there was little to inspire, and nothing to justify, a troubled conscience in the proposals that our government made to the United Nations, as to the form which the international control of atomic energy should take. These proposals, and some detailed means for implementing them, were explored and criticized, elaborated, and recommended for adoption by fourteen of the seventeen member nations who served on the United Nations Atomic Energy Commission. They were rejected as wholly unacceptable, even as a basis for further discussion, by the three Soviet states, whose contributions to policy and to debate have throughout constituted for us a debasingly low standard of comparison.

This September, the Commission made its third, and what it thought its final, report to the General Assembly, meeting in Paris. It recommended to the Assembly that the general outlines of the proposed form of international control be endorsed, that the inadequacy of the Soviet counterproposals be noted, and that the Commission itself be permitted to discontinue its work pending either a satisfactory prior negotiation between the permanent members of the Security Council and Canada, or the finding by the General Assembly that the general political conditions which had in the past obstructed progress had been so far altered that agreement now appeared possible. The Assembly did in fact accept all the recommendations but one. It asked the Commission to continue meeting. In its instructions to the Commission, however, the Assembly failed to provide affirmative indications of what the Commission was to do, or to express any confidence in the success of its further efforts; in fact, one might dismiss this action as no more than an indication of unwillingness on the part of the Assembly to accept as permanent the obvious past failures of the Commission to fulfill its mandate.

Yet we may recognize that more is involved in this action, that we will come to understand in the measure in which the nature and purposes of our own preoccupation with the problem become clearer. In part at least the Assembly asked that this problem of the atom not be let lapse because it touches in a most intimate, if sometimes symbolic, way the profoundest questions of international affairs; because the Assembly wished to reaffirm that these problems could not be dismissed, that these issues could not be lost, whatever the immediate frustrations and however obscure the prospects. The Assembly was in fact asking that we let time and nature, and human reason and good example as a part of that nature, play some part in fulfilling the age-old aspirations of man for preserving the peace.

In any political action, and surely in one as complex and delicate as the international act and commitment made by the United States with regard to atomic energy, far more is always involved than can or should be isolated in a brief analysis. Despite all hysteria, there is some truth to the view that the steps which we took with regard to atomic energy could be understood in terms of the terror of atomic warfare. We have sought to avert this; we have further sought to avert the probable adverse consequences of atomic armament for our own institutions and our freedom. Yet more basic and more general issues are involved, which, though symbolized and rendered critical by the development of atomic energy, are in their nature not confined to it; they pervade almost all the key problems of foreign policy. If we are to seek a clue to the misgivings with which we tend to look at ourselves, we may, I think, find it just in the manner in which we have dealt, in their wider contexts, with these basic themes.

The first has to do with the role of coercion in human affairs; the second with the role of openness. The atomic bomb, born of a way of life, fostered throughout the centuries, in which the role of coercion was perhaps reduced more completely than in any other human activity, and which owed its whole success and its very existence to the possibility of open discussion and free inquiry, appeared in a strange paradox, at once a secret, and an unparalleled instrument of coercion.

These two mutually interdependent ideals, the minimization of coercion and the minimization of secrecy, are, of course, in the nature of things, not absolute; any attempt to erect them as absolute will induce in us that vertigo which warns us that we are near the limits of intelligible definition. But they are very deep in our ethical as well as in our political traditions, and are recorded in earnest, eloquent simplicity in the words of those who founded this nation. They are in fact inseparable from the idea of the dignity of man to which our country, in its beginnings, was dedicated, and which has proved the monitor of our vigor and of our health. These two ideals are closely related, the one pointing toward persuasion as the key to political action, the other to free discussion and knowledge as the essential instrument of persuasion. They are so deep within us that we seldom find it necessary, and perhaps seldom possible, to talk of them. When they are challenged by tyranny abroad or by malpractice at home, we come back to them as the wardens of our public life—as for many of us they are as well wardens of our lives as men.

In foreign affairs, we are not unfamiliar with either the use or the need of power. Yet we are stubbornly distrustful of it. We seem to know, and seem to come back again and again to this knowledge, that the purposes of this country in the field of foreign policy cannot in any real or enduring way be achieved by coercion.

We have a natural sympathy for extending to foreign affairs what we have come to learn so well in our political life at home: that an indispensable, perhaps in some ways *the* indispensable, element in giving meaning to the dignity of man, and in making possible the taking of decision on the basis of honest conviction, is the openness of men's minds, and the openness of whatever media there are for communion between men, free of restraint, free of repression, and free even of that most pervasive of all restraints, that of status and of hierarchy.

In the days of the founding of this republic, in all of the eighteenth century which was formative for the growth and the explicit formulation of our political ideals, politics and science were of a piece. The hope that this might in some sense again be so, was stirred to new life by the development of atomic energy. In this it has throughout been decisive that openness, openness in the first instance with regard to technical problems and to the actual undertakings underway in various parts of the world, was the one single essential precondition for a measure of security in the atomic age. Here we met in uniquely comprehensible form the alternatives of common understanding, or of the practices of secrecy and of force.

In all this I pretend to be saying nothing new, nothing that has not been known to all thoughtful men since the days of Hiroshima; yet it has seldom come to expression; it has been overlaid with other preoccupations, perhaps equally necessary to the elaboration of an effective international control, but far less decisive in determining whether such a control could exist. It is just because it has not been possible to obtain assent, even in principle, even as an honest statement of intent or purpose, to these basic theses that the deadlock in attempting to establish control has appeared so serious, so refractory, and so enduring.

These words have an intent quite contrary to the creation of a sense of panic or of doom. Yet we need to start with the admission that we see no clear course before us that would persuade the governments of the world to join with us in creating a more and more open world, and thus to establish the foundation on which persuasion might so largely replace coercion in determining human affairs. We ourselves have acknowledged this grim prospect, and responded by adopting some of the very measures that we had hoped might be universally renounced. With misgivings—and there ought to be misgivings—we are rearming, arming atomically, as in other fields. With deep misgivings, we are keeping secret not only those elements of our military plans, but those elements of our technical information and policy, a knowledge of which would render us more subject to enemy coercion and less effective in exercising our own. There are not many men who see an acceptable alternative to this course, although there apparently are some who would regard it as a proof of the shallowness and insincerity of our earlier renunciation of these ways. But whether, among our own people or among our friends abroad or even among those who are not our friends, these measures which we are taking appear excessive, or on the whole insufficient, they must have at least one effect. Inevitably they must appear to commit us to a future of secrecy, and to an immanent threat of war. It is true that one may hear arguments that the mere existence of our power, quite apart from its exercise, may turn the world to the ways of openness and of peace. Yet we have today no clear, no formulated, no in some measure credible account of how this may come about. We have chosen to read, and perhaps we have correctly read, our past as a lesson that a policy of weakness has failed us. But we have not read the future as an intelligible lesson that a policy of strength can save us.

When the time is run, and that future become history, it will be clear how little of it we today foresaw or could foresee. How then can we preserve hope and sensitiveness which could enable us to take advantage of all that it has in store? Our problem is not only to face the somber and the grim elements of the future, but to keep them from obscuring it.

Our recent election has seemed to touch this deep sense of the imponderable in the history of the future, this understanding that we must not preclude the cultivation of any unexpected, hopeful turnings. Immediately after the election people seemed stirred, less even by the outcome itself, than by the element of wonder; they would tend to say things like: "Well, after this perhaps we need not be so sure that there will be a war." This sense that the future is richer and more complex than our prediction of it, and that wisdom lies in sensitiveness to what is new and hopeful, is perhaps a sign of some maturity in politics.

The problem of doing justice to the implicit, the imponderable, and the unknown is of course not unique to politics. It is always with us in science, it is with us in the most trivial of personal affairs, and it is one of the great problems of writing and of all forms of art. The means by which it is solved is sometimes called style. It is style which complements affirmation with limitation and with humility; it is style which makes it possible to act effectively, but not absolutely; it is style which, in the domain of foreign policy, enables us to find a harmony between the pursuit of ends essential to us, and the regard for the views, the sensibilities, the aspirations of those to whom the problem may appear in another light; it is style which is the deference that action pays to uncertainty; it is above all style through which power defers to reason.

We need to remember that we are a powerful nation.

We need to remember that when the future that we can now foresee deviates so markedly from all that we hope and all that we value, we can, by our example, and by the mode and the style with which we conduct our affairs, let it be apparent that we have not abandoned those hopes nor forsaken those values; we need to do this even while concrete steps, to which we resort to avert more immediate disaster, seem to negate them.

Our past is rich in example. In that other agony, the Civil War, where the foundations of our government were proved and reaffirmed, it was Lincoln who again and again struck true the balance between power and reason. By 1863, the war and the blockade had deepened the attrition of the South. They had also stopped the supplies of cotton to the English mills. Early that year Lincoln wrote a letter to the working men of Manchester. He wrote:

". . . It is not always in the power of governments to enlarge or restrict the scope of moral results which follow the policies that they may deem it necessary for the public safety from time to time to adopt.

"I have understood well that the duty of self-preservation rests solely with the American people; but I have at the same time been aware that favor or disfavor of foreign nations might have a material influence in enlarging or prolonging the struggle with disloyal men in which the country is engaged. A fair examination of history has served to authorize a belief that the past actions and influences of the United States were generally regarded as having been beneficial toward mankind. I have, therefore, reckoned upon the forbearance of nations . . ."

Fifteen months later, a year before Lincoln's death, the battle had turned. He could say:

". . . When the war began, three years ago, neither party, nor any man, expected it would last till now. Each looked for the end in some way, long ere today. Neither did any anticipate that domestic slavery would be much affected by the war. But here we are; the war has not ended, and slavery has been much affected—how much needs not now to be recounted . . .

"But we can see the past, though we may not claim to have

directed it; and seeing it, in this case, we feel more hopeful and confident for the future . . ."

In such magnanimity even Grant, at Appomattox a year later, looking beyond the bitter slaughter, looking to nature and to time, could speak to Lee: His troops were to keep their horses; they would need them for the spring plowing.

Each of us, recalling our actions in these last critical years, will be able to find more than one instance where, in the formulation or implementation of policy, we have been worthy of this past. Each of us will mourn the opportunities that may seem to him lost, the doors once open and now closed. Not even in critical times can the sense of style, the open mind, be fostered by issuing directives; nor can they rest wholly on soliciting great actions not yet taken, great words not yet spoken. If they were wholly a matter for one man, all could well rest on his wisdom and his sensitiveness —they neither are, nor can, nor should be. The spirit in which our foreign affairs are conducted will in the large reflect the understanding and the desires of our people; and their concrete, detailed administration will necessarily rest in the hands of countless men and women, officials of the government, who constitute the branches of our foreign service, of our State Department, and of the many agencies which now supplement the State Department, at home and abroad. The style, the perceptiveness, the imagination and the open-mindedness with which we need to conduct our affairs can only pervade such a complex of organizations, consisting inevitably of men of varied talent, taste and character, if it is a reflection of a deep and widespread public understanding. That is why, despite their sketchiness, it has seemed appropriate to present these views to a group of interested and devoted citizens. It is in our hands to see that the hope of the future is not lost, because we were too sure that we knew the answers, too sure that there was no hope.

IV

Atomic Weapons and American Policy

THIS LECTURE *was originally delivered before the Council on Foreign Relations in New York City on February 17, 1953, and was later published in that organization's quarterly* Foreign Affairs.

IV

Atomic Weapons and American Policy

It is possible that in the large light of history, if indeed there is to be history, the atomic bomb will appear not very different than in the bright light of the first atomic explosion. Partly because of the mood of the time, partly because of a very clear prevision of what the technical developments would be, we had the impression that this might mark, not merely the end of a great and terrible war, but the end of such wars for mankind.

Two years later Colonel Stimson was to write in *Foreign Affairs:* "The riven atom, uncontrolled, can be only a growing menace to us all . . ." In the same paragraph he wrote, "Lasting peace and freedom cannot be achieved until the world finds a way toward the necessary government of the whole." * Earlier, shortly after the war's end, the government of the United States had put forward some modest suggestions, responsive to these views, for dealing with the atom in a friendly, open, co-operative way. We need not argue as to whether these proposals were stillborn. They have been very dead a long, long time, to the surprise of only a few. Openness, friendliness and co-operation did not seem to be what the Soviet government most prized on this earth.

It should not be beyond human ingenuity for us to devise less friendly proposals. We need not here detail the many reasons why they have not been put forward, why it has appeared irrelevant and grotesque to do so. These reasons range from the special difficulties of all negotiation with the Soviet Union, through the peculiar obstacles presented by the programmatic hostility and the institutionalized secretiveness of communist countries, to what may be regarded as the more normal and familiar difficulties of devising instruments for the regulation of armaments in a world without prospect of political settlement.

Instead we came to grips, or began to come to grips, with the massive evidences of Soviet hostility, and the growing evidences of Soviet power, and with the many almost inevitable, yet often tragic, elements of weakness, disharmony

* "The Challenge to Americans," by Henry L. Stimson. *Foreign Affairs*, October 1947.

and disunity in what we have learned to call the Free World.

In these preoccupations—one wholly negative, and one largely positive though very difficult—the atom, too, was given a simple role, and the policy followed was a fairly simple one. The role was to be one ingredient of a shield: a shield composed also in part of the great industrial power of America, and in part of the military and, even more, the political weaknesses of the Soviet Union. The rule for the atom was: "Let us keep ahead. Let us be sure that we are ahead of the enemy."

Today it would seem that, however necessary these considerations and these policies may be, they are no longer nearly sufficient. The reason for that one can see when one looks at the character of the arms race. The reason for that one can see when one compares the time-scale of atomic developments here and abroad with the probable time-scale of deep political changes in the world.

It is easy to say "Let us look at the arms race." I must tell about it without communicating anything. I must reveal its nature without revealing anything; and this I propose to do.

There are three countries embarked on this race: The United Kingdom—and of that we need to note only that it is unfortunate that so talented and hard-pressed a country, so close to us in history and tradition, should be doing all this separately from us—ourselves, and the U.S.S.R.

As for the U.S.S.R., it has recently been said officially, and thus may be repeated with official sanction, that it has produced three atomic explosions, and is producing fissionable material in substantial quantities. I should like to present the evidence for this; I cannot. We do need one word of warning: This is evidence which could well be evidence of what the government of the U.S.S.R. wants us to think, rather than evidence of what is true. I may, however, record my own casual, perhaps too rough guess as to how the U.S.S.R. stands in relation to us in this field of atomic munitions. This does not refer at all to other elements of armament. I think that the U.S.S.R. is about four years behind us. And I think that the scale of its operations is not as big as ours was four years ago. It may be something like half as big as ours then was. This is consistent with the facts known to us. It has not been proven by them, by any means.

This sounds comfortably reassuring. It sounds as though the job of keeping ahead were being satisfactorily accomplished. But in order to assay what it means, we have to know something of what it is that they are four years behind, how fast the situation is likely to change, and what it means to be half as big as we are.

When Hiroshima was bombed there was a single plane. There was no air opposition. We flew straight in at medium height, at rather low speed, over the city of Hiroshima; we dropped one bomb with an energy release the equivalent of about fifteen thousand tons of TNT. It killed more than seventy thousand people and produced a comparable number of casualties; it largely destroyed a medium-sized city. That we had in mind. But we also had in mind, and we said, that it was not a question of one bomb. It would become a question of ten, and then one hundred, and then a thousand, and then ten thousand, and then maybe one hundred thousand. We knew—or, rather, we did not know, but we had very good reason to think—that it was not a question of ten thousand tons but of one hundred thousand and then a million tons, and then ten million tons and then maybe one hundred million tons.

We knew that these munitions could be adapted, not merely to a slow medium bomber operating where we had almost complete air supremacy, but to methods of delivery more modern, more flexible, harder to intercept, and more suitable for combat as it might be encountered today.

Today all of this is in train. It is my opinion that we should all know—not precisely, but quantitatively and, above all, authoritatively—where we stand in these matters; that we should all have a good idea of how rapidly the situation has changed, and of where we may stand, let us say, three, four, or five years ahead, which is about as far as one can see. I shall revert to the reasons why I think it important that we all know of these matters. I cannot write of them.

What I can say is this: I have never discussed these prospects candidly with any responsible group, whether scientists or statesmen, whether citizens or officers of the government, with any group that could steadily look at the facts, that did not come away with a great sense of anxiety and somberness at what they saw. The very least we can say is that, looking ten years ahead, it is likely to be small comfort that the Soviet Union is four years behind us, and small comfort that they are only about half as big as we are. The very least we can conclude is that our twenty-thousandth bomb, useful as it may be in filling the vast munitions pipelines of a great war, will not in any deep strategic sense offset their two-thousandth. The very least we can say is that, as Mr. Gordon Dean has emphasized, there will come a time when, even from the narrowest technical point of view, the art of delivery and the art of defense will have a much higher military relevance than supremacy in the atomic munitions field itself.

There are other aspects of the arms race; though they may be well known, they are worth mentioning. We developed the atomic bomb under the stimulus of the fear that the Germans might be at it. We deliberated at length on the use of the bomb against Japan; indeed it was Colonel Stimson who initiated and presided over these thorough deliberations. We decided that it should be used. We have greatly developed and greatly increased our atomic activities. This growth, though natural technically, is not inevitable. If the Congress had appropriated no money, it would not have occurred. We have made our decision to push our stockpiles and the power of our weapons. We have from the first maintained that we should be free to use these weapons; and it is generally known we plan to use them. It is also generally known that one ingredient of this plan is a rather rigid commitment to their use in a very massive, initial, unremitting strategic assault on the enemy.

This arms race has other characteristics. There has been relatively little done to secure our defense against the atom;

and in the far more tragic and difficult problem of defending our allies in Europe still less has been done. This does not promise to be an easy problem.

Atomic weapons are not just one element of an arsenal that we hope may deter the Soviet government, or just one of the means we think of for putting an end to a war, once started. It is, perhaps, almost the only military measure that anyone has in mind to prevent, let us say, a great battle in Europe from being a continuing, agonizing, large-scale Korea. It is the only military instrument which brings the Soviet Union and the United States into contact—a most uncomfortable and dangerous contact—with one another.

Atomic weapons, as everyone knows, have been incorporated in the plans for the defense of Europe. They have been developed for many tactical military uses, as in the antisubmarine campaign, the air campaign, and the ground campaign in the European theater; and these potential applications continue to ramify and multiply. Yet the Europeans are rather in ignorance of what these weapons are, how many there may be, how they will be used and what they will do. It thus needs to be remarked, as we shall need to remark again, that for Europe, the atomic weapon is both a much needed hope of effective defense and a terrible immediate peril, greater even than for this country.

These are some of the peculiarities of this arms race, marked for us by a very great rigidity of policy, and a terrifyingly rapid accumulation, probably on both sides, of a deadly munition. When we think of the terms in which we in this country tend to talk of the future, the somberness with which thoughtful men leave a discussion of the subject is not wholly ununderstandable. There are two things that everyone would like to see happen; but few people, if any, confidently believe that they will happen soon. One is a prompt, a happily prompt reform or collapse of the enemy. One is a regulation of armaments as part of a general political settlement —an acceptable, hopeful, honorable and humane settlement to which we could be a party.

There is nothing repugnant in these prospects; but they may not appear to be very likely in the near future. Most of us, and almost all Europeans, appear to regard the outbreak of war in this near future as a disaster. Thus the prevailing view is that we are probably faced with a long period of cold war in which conflict, tension and armaments are to be with us. The trouble then is just this: During this period the atomic clock ticks faster and faster; we may anticipate a state of affairs in which two Great Powers will each be in a position to put an end to the civilization and life of the other, though not without risking its own. We may be likened to two scorpions in a bottle, each capable of killing the other, but only at the risk of his own life.

This prospect does not tend to make for serenity; and the basic fact that needs to be communicated is that the time in which this will happen is short, compared to the time in which reasonable men may have some confidence in a reasonable amelioration or even alteration of the great political troubles of our time.

In this prospect, surely, we shall need all the help and wisdom and resourcefulness we can muster. This, in all probability, is a very tough fix. There are three things we need to remember, three things that are very sharp. It is perilous to forget any one of them. One is the hostility and the power of the Soviet. Another is the touch of weakness—the need for unity, the need for some stability, the need for armed strength on the part of our friends in the Free World. And the third is the increasing peril of the atom.

It is straightforward, if not easy, if we forget the last. It is easy if we forget the first. It is hard if we remember all three. But they are all there.

We need the greatest attainable freedom of action. We need strength to be able to ask whether our plans for the use of the atom are, all things considered, right or wrong. We need the freedom of action necessary—and we do not have it today—to be able to negotiate, should an opportunity for that at some future time appear.

Much will be needed to bring us this freedom of action. Some of it we cannot write about because it has not occurred to us. Some we cannot write about because it would not be proper for anything but official discussion. An example may be the question of whether, under what circumstances, in what manner, and with what purpose to communicate with the Soviet government on this and related problems.

But there are three reforms which seem so obvious, so important, so sure to be salutary that I should like to discuss them briefly. One has to do with making available to ourselves, in this tough time, the inherent resources of a country like ours and a government like ours. These resources are not available today. The second has to do with making available the resources of a coalition of governments, bound together in an alliance, yet at the moment foreclosed from discussing one of the principal factors that affects the destiny of the alliance and of all its members. The third has to do with taking measures to put off, to moderate, to reduce the dangers of which we have spoken. I shall deal with each of these.

The first is candor—candor on the part of the officials of the United States government to the officials, the representatives, the people of their country. We do not operate well when the important facts, the essential conditions, which limit and determine our choice are unknown. We do not operate well when they are known, in secrecy and in fear, only to a few men.

The general account of the atomic arms race that has been outlined here can, of course, be found in the public press, together with a great deal of detailed information, some true, and much largely false. This mass of published rumor, fact, press release and speculation could yield, upon analysis, a fairly solid core of truth; but as it stands, it is not the truth. The consequences of such ignorance may seem obvious; but we may recall two examples that illustrate well what they are.

It must be disturbing that an ex-President of the United States, who has been briefed on what we know about the Soviet atomic capability, can publicly call in doubt all conclusions from the evidence. Perhaps this was primarily because it was all so secret that it could not be talked about, or thought about, or understood. It must be shocking when this doubt, so recently expressed, is compounded by two men, one of them a most distinguished scientist, who headed one of the great projects of the Manhattan District during the war, and one of them a brilliant officer, who was in over-all charge of the Manhattan District. These two men are not now employed by any agency of the government concerned with these questions; therefore they did not have access to the evidence. Thus their advice is unavailing, their public counsel wrong.

A second example may illustrate further. A high officer of the Air Defense Command said—and this only a few months ago, in a most serious discussion of measures for the continental defense of the United States—that it was our policy to attempt to protect our striking force, but not really our policy to attempt to protect this country, for that is so big a job that it would interfere with our retaliatory capabilities. Such follies can occur only when even the men who know the facts can find no one to talk to about them, when the facts are too secret for discussion, and thus for thought.

The political vitality of our country largely derives from two sources. One is the interplay, the conflict of opinion and debate, in many diverse and complex agencies, legislative and executive, which contribute to the making of policy. The other is a public opinion which is based on confidence that it knows the truth.

Today public opinion cannot exist in this field. No responsible person will hazard an opinion in a field where he believes that there is somebody else who knows the truth, and where he believes that he does not know it. It is true that there are and always will be, as long as we live in danger of war, secrets that it is important to keep secret, at least for an appropriate period, if not for all time; some of these, and important ones, are in the field of atomic energy. But knowledge of the characteristics and probable effects of our atomic weapons, of—in rough terms—the numbers available, and of the changes that are likely to occur within the next years, this is not among the things to be kept secret. Nor is our general estimate of where the enemy stands.

Many arguments have been advanced against making public this basic information. Some of these arguments had merit in times past. One is that we might be giving vital information to the enemy. My own view is that the enemy has this information. It is available to anyone who will trouble to make an intelligence analysis of what has been published. Private citizens do not do this; but we must expect that the enemy does. It is largely available by other means as well. It is also my view that it is good for the peace of the world if the enemy knows these basic facts—very good indeed, and very dangerous if he does not.

There is another source of worry—that public knowledge of the situation might induce in this country a mood of despair, or a too ready acceptance of what is lightheartedly called preventive war. I believe that until we have looked this tiger in the eye, we shall be in the worst of all possible dangers, which is that we may back into him. More generally, I do not think a country like ours can in any real sense survive if we are afraid of our people.

As a first step, but a great one, we need the courage and the wisdom to make public at least what, in all reason, the enemy must now know: To describe in rough but authoritative and quantitative terms what the atomic armaments race is. It is not enough to say, as our government so often has, that we have made "substantial progress." When the American people are responsibly informed, we may not have solved, but we shall have a new freedom to face, some of the tough problems that are before us.

There is also need for candor in our dealings at least with our major allies. The Japanese are exposed to atomic bombardment; and it may be very hard to develop adequate countermeasures. Space, that happy asset of the United States, is not an asset for Japan. It is not an asset for France. It is not an asset for England. There are in existence methods of delivery of atomic weapons which present an intractable problem of interception, and which are relevant for the small distances that characterize Europe. It will be some time at least before they are relevant for intercontinental delivery. These countries will one day feel a terrible pinch, when the U.S.S.R. chooses to remind them of what it can do, and do very easily—not without suffering, but in a way that the Europeans themselves can little deter or deflect.

There have been arguments for technical collaboration with the United Kingdom and Canada; these have often appeared persuasive. There have been arguments for military collaboration with the NATO governments, and with the responsible commanders involved; General Bradley and General Collins both have spoken of this need, partly in order to explain to our allies that an atomic bomb will not do all things—that it has certain capabilities but it is not the whole answer. This is surely a precondition for effective planning, and for the successful defense of Europe.

Yet there are much more general reasons. We and our allies are in this long struggle together. What we do will affect the destiny of Europe; what is done there will affect ours; and we cannot operate wisely if a large half of the problem we have in common is not discussed in common. This does not mean that we should tie our hands. It means that we should inform and consult. This could make a healthy and perhaps very great change in our relations with Europe.

It is not clear that the situation even in the Far East would be wholly unaffected. It is troublesome to read that a principal reason that we should not use atomic weapons in Korea is that our allies would not like it. We need not argue here either that it is right or that it is wrong to use them there. In either case, our decisions should rest on far firmer ground than that other governments, who know less than we about the matter, should hold a different view than ours. It would be proper that the Japanese and the British and the many other governments immediately involved have a notion of what the issues really are.

Once, clearly, the problem of proper candor at home is faced—the problem of a more reasonable behavior toward our own people and our representatives and officials with regard to the atom—then the problem of dealing with our allies will be less troublesome. For it is pretty much the same information, the same rough set of facts, that both our people and our allies need to have and to understand.

The third point may seem even more obvious. I do not believe—though of course we cannot today be certain—that we can take measures for the defense of our people, our lives, our institutions, our cities, which will in any real sense be a permanent solution to the problem of the atom. But that is no reason for not doing a little better than we are now doing.

The current view, as is well known, is not very optimistic. Not long ago General Vandenberg estimated that we might, with luck, intercept twenty or thirty per cent of an enemy attack. That is not very reassuring, when one looks at numbers and casualties, and what it takes to destroy the heart and life of our country. For some months now, a highly qualified panel, under the chairmanship of Dr. Mervin Kelly, appointed by Secretary Lovett and reporting now to Secretary Wilson, has studied the complex technical problems of continental defense. There are many technical developments that have not yet been applied in this field, and that could well be helpful. They are natural but substantial developments in munitions, in aircraft and in missiles, and in procedures for obtaining and analyzing information. Above all, there is the challenging problem of the effective use of space; there is space between the Soviet Union and the United States. This panel, it would appear, has been oppressed and troubled by the same over-all oppression which any group always finds, when it touches seriously any part of the problem of the atom. Yet there is no doubt that it will recommend sensible ways in which we can proceed to try to defend our lives and our country.

Such measures will inevitably have many diverse meanings. They will mean, first of all, some delay in the imminence of the threat. They will mean a disincentive—a defensive deterrent—to the Soviet Union. They will mean that the time when the Soviet Union can be confident of destroying the productive power of America will be somewhat further off—very much further off than if we did nothing. They will mean, even to our allies, who are much more exposed and probably cannot be well defended, that the continued existence of a real and strong America will be a solid certainty which should discourage the outbreak of war.

A more effective defense could even be of great relevance, should the time come for serious discussion of the regulation of armaments. There will have been by then a vast accumulation of materials for atomic weapons, and a troublesome margin of uncertainty with regard to its accounting—very troublesome indeed if we still live with vestiges of the suspicion, the hostility and secretiveness of the world of today. This will call for a very broad and robust regulation of armaments, in which existing forces and weapons are of a wholly different order than those required for the destruction of one great nation by another, in which steps of evasion will be either far too vast to conceal or far too small to have, in view of then existing measures of defense, a decisive strategic effect. Defense and regulation may thus be necessary complements. And here, too, all that we do effectively to contribute to our own immunity will be helpful in giving us some measure of an increased freedom of action.

These are three paths that we may take. None of them is a wholly new suggestion. They have, over the long years, been discussed; but they have not been acted on. In my opinion they have not, in any deep sense, been generally understood. We need to be clear that there will not be many great atomic wars for us, nor for our institutions. It is important that there not be one. We need to liberate our own great resources, to shape our destiny.

V

Physics in the Contemporary World

THIS LECTURE *was delivered on November 25, 1947, as the second Arthur Dehon Little Memorial Lecture at the Massachusetts Institute of Technology in Cambridge.*

V

Physics in the Contemporary World

If I have even in the title of this talk sought to restrict its theme, that does not imply an overestimate of physics among the sciences, nor a too great myopia for these contemporary days. It is rather that I must take my starting point in the science in which I have lived and worked, and a time through which my colleagues and I are living.

Nevertheless, I shall be talking tonight about things which are quite general for the relations between science and civilization. For it would seem that in the ways of science, its practice, the peculiarities of its discipline and universality, there are patterns which in the past have somewhat altered, and in the future may greatly alter, all that we think about the world and how we manage to live in it. What I shall be able to say of this will not be rich in exhortation, for this is ground that I know how to tread only very lightly.

But that I should be speaking of such general and such difficult questions at all reflects in the first instance a good deal of self-consciousness on the part of physicists. This self-consciousness is in part a result of the highly critical traditions which have grown up in physics in the last half century, which have shown in so poignant a way how much the applications of science determine our welfare and that of our fellows, and which have cast in doubt that traditional optimism, that confidence in progress, which have characterized Western culture since the Renaissance.

It is, then, *about* physics rather than *of* physics that I shall be speaking—and there is a great deal of difference. You know that when a student of physics makes his first acquaintance with the theory of atomic structure and of quanta, he must come to understand the rather deep and subtle notion which has turned out to be the clue to unraveling that whole domain of physical experience. This is the notion of complementarity, which recognizes that various ways of talking about physical experience may each have validity, and may each be necessary for the adequate description of the physical world, and may yet stand in a mutually exclusive relationship to each other, so that to a situation to which one applies, there may be no consistent possibility of applying the other. Teachers very often try to find illustrations, familiar from experience, for relationships of this kind; and one of the most apt is the exclusive relationship between the practicing of an art and the description of that practice. Both are a part of civilized life. But an analysis of what we do and the doing of it—these are hard to bed in the same bed.

As it did on everything else, the last world war had a great and at least a temporarily disastrous effect on the prosecution of pure science. The demands of military technology in this country and in Britain, the equally overriding demands of the Resistance in much of Europe, distracted the physicists from their normal occupations, as they distracted most other men.

We in this country, who take our wars rather spastically, perhaps witnessed a more total cessation of true professional activity in the field of physics, even in its training, than did any other people. For in all the doings of war we, as a country, have been a little like the young physicist who went to Washington to work for the National Defense Research Committee in 1940. There he met his first Civil Service questionnaire and came to the questions on drinking: "Never," "occasionally," "habitually," "to excess." He checked both "occasionally" and to "to excess." So, in the past, we have taken war.

All over the world, whether because of the closing of universities, or the distractions of scientists called in one way or another to serve their countries, or because of devastation and terror and attrition, there was a great gap in physical science. It has been an exciting and an inspiring sight to watch the recovery—a recovery testifying to extraordinary vitality and vigor in this human activity. Today, barely two years after the end of hostilities, physics is booming.

One may have gained the impression that this boom derives primarily from the application of the new techniques developed during the war, such as the atomic reactor and microwave equipment; one may have gained the impression that in large part the flourishing of physics lies in exploitation of the eagerness of governments to promote it. These are indeed important factors. But they are only a small part of the story. Without in any way deprecating the great value of wartime technology, one nevertheless sees how much of what is today new knowledge can trace its origin directly, by an orderly yet imaginative extension, to the kind of things that physicists were doing in their laboratories and with their pencils almost a decade ago.

Let me try to give a little more substance to the physics that is booming. We are continuing the attempt to discover, to identify and characterize, and surely ultimately to order, our knowledge of what the elementary particles of physics really are. I need hardly say that in the course of this we are learning again how far our notion of *elementarity*, of what makes a particle elementary, is from the early atomic ideas of the Hindu and Greek atomists, or even from the chemical atomists of a century ago. We are finding out that what we are forced to call elementary particles retain neither permanence nor identity, and they are elementary only in the sense that their properties cannot be understood by breaking them down into subcomponents. Almost every month has surprises for us in the findings about these particles. We are meeting new ones for which we are not prepared. We are learning how poorly we had identified the properties even of our old friends among them. We are seeing what a challenging job the ordering of this experience is likely to be, and what a strange world we must enter to find that order.

In penetrating into this world perhaps our sharpest tool in the past has been the observation of the phenomena of the cosmic rays in interaction with matter. But the next years will see an important methodological improvement, when the great program of ultra-high-energy accelerators begins to get under way. This program is itself one of the expensive parts of physics. It has been greatly subsidized by the government, primarily through the Atomic Energy Commission and the Office of Naval Research. It is a superlative example, of which one could find so many, of the repayment that technology makes to basic science, in providing means whereby our physical experience can be extended and enriched.

Another progress is the definement of our knowledge of the behavior of electrons within atomic systems, a refinement which on the one hand is based on the microwave techniques, to the developments of which the Radiation Laboratory of the Massachusetts Institute of Technology made unique contributions, and which on the other hand has provided a newly vigorous criterion for the adequacy of our knowledge of the interactions of radiation and matter. Thus we are beginning to see in this field at least a partial resolution, and I am myself inclined to think rather more than that, of the paradoxes that have plagued the professional physical theorists for two decades.

A third advance in atomic physics is in the increasing understanding of those forces which give to atomic nuclei their great stability, and to their transmutations their great violence. It is the prevailing view that a true understanding of these forces may well not be separable from the ordering of our experience with regard to elementary particles, and that it may also turn on an extension to new fields of recent advances in electrodynamics.

However this may be, all of us who are physicists by profession know that we are embarked on another great adventure of exploration and understanding, and count ourselves happy for that.

In how far is this an account of physics in the United States only? In how far does it apply to other parts of the world, more seriously ravaged and more deeply disturbed by the last war? That question may have a somewhat complex answer, to the varied elements of which one may pay respectful attention.

In much of Europe and in Japan, that part of physics which does not rest on the availability of elaborate and radical new equipment is enjoying a recovery comparable to our own. The traditional close associations of workers in various countries makes it just as difficult now to disentangle the contributions by nationality as it was in the past. But there can be little doubt that it is very much harder for a physicist in France, for instance, or the Low Countries, and very much more nearly impossible for him in Japan, to build a giant accelerator than it is for the workers in this country.

Yet in those areas of the world where science has not merely been disturbed or arrested by war and by terror, but where terror and its official philosophy have, in a deep sense, corrupted its very foundations, even the traditional fraternity of scientists has not proved adequate protection against decay. It may not be clear to us in what way and to what extent the spirit of scientific inquiry may come to apply to matters not yet and perhaps never to be part of the domain of science; but that it does apply, there is one very brutal indication. Tyranny, when it gets to be absolute, or when it tends so to become, finds it impossible to continue to live with science.

Even in the good ways of contemporary physics, we are reluctantly made aware of our dependence on things which lie outside our science. The experience of the war, for those who were called upon to serve the survival of their civilization through the Resistance, and for those who contributed more remotely, if far more decisively, by the development of new instruments and weapons of war, has left us with a legacy of concern. In these troubled times it is not likely that we shall be free of it altogether. Nor perhaps is it right that we should be.

Nowhere is this troubled sense of responsibility more acute, and surely nowhere has it been more prolix, than among those who participated in the development of atomic energy for military purposes. I should think that most historians would agree that other technical developments, notably radar, played a more decisive part in determining the outcome of this last war. But I doubt whether that participation would have of itself created the deep trouble and moral concern which so many of us who were physicists have felt, have voiced, and have tried to get over feeling. It is not hard to understand why this should be so. The physics which played the decisive part in the development of the atomic bomb came straight out of war laboratories and our journals.

Despite the vision and the far-seeing wisdom of our wartime heads of state, the physicists felt a peculiarly intimate responsibility for suggesting, for supporting, and in the end, in large measure, for achieving the realization of atomic weapons. Nor can we forget that these weapons, as they were in fact used, dramatized so mercilessly the inhumanity and evil of modern war. In some sort of crude sense which no vulgarity, no humor, no overstatement can quite extinguish, the physicists have known sin; and this is a knowledge which they cannot lose.

Probably in giving expression to such feelings of concern most of us have belabored the influence of science on society through the medium of technology. This is natural, since the developments of the war years were almost exclusively technological, and since the participation of academic scientists forced to be deeply aware of an activity of whose existence they had always known but which had been often remote from them.

When I was a student at Göttingen twenty years ago, there was a story current about the great mathematician Hilbert, who perhaps would have liked, had the world let him, to have thought of his science as something independent of worldly vicissitudes. Hilbert had a colleague, an equally eminent mathematician, Felix Klein, who was certainly aware, if not of the dependence of science generally on society, at least of the dependence of mathematics on the physical sciences which nourish it and give it application. Klein used to take some of his students to meet once a year with the engineers of the Technical High School in Hanover. One year he was ill and asked Hilbert to go in his stead, and urged him, in the little talk that he would give, to try to refute the then prevalent notion that there was a basic hostility between science and technology. Hilbert promised to do so; but when the time came a magnificent absent-mindedness led him instead to speak his own mind: "One hears a good deal nowadays of the hostility between science and technology. I don't think that is true, gentlemen. I am quite sure that it isn't true, gentlemen. It almost certainly isn't true. It really can't be true. *Sie haben ja gar nichts mit einander zu tun.* They have nothing whatever to do with one another." Today the wars and the troubled times deny us the luxury of such absent-mindedness.

The great testimony of history shows how often in fact the development of science has emerged in response to technological and even economic needs, and how in the economy of social effort, science, even of the most abstract and recondite kind, pays for itself again and again in providing the basis for radically new technological developments. In fact, most people—when they think of science as a good thing, when they think of it as worthy of encouragement, when they are willing to see their governments spend substance upon it, when they greatly do honor to men who in science have attained some eminence—have in mind that the conditions of their life have been altered just by such technology, of which they may be reluctant to be deprived.

The debt of science to technology is just as great. Even the most abstract researches owe their very existence to things that have taken place quite outside of science, and with the primary purpose of altering and improving the conditions of man's life. As long as there is a healthy physics, this mutual fructification will surely continue. Out of its work there will come in the future, as so often in the past, and with an apparently chaotic unpredictability, things which will improve man's health, ease his labor, and divert and edify him. There will come things which, properly handled, will shorten his working day and take away the most burdensome part of his effort, which will enable him to communicate, to travel, and to have a wider choice both in the general question of how he is to spend his life and in the specific question of how he is to spend an hour of his leisure. There is no need to belabor this point, nor its obverse—that out of science there will come, as there has in this last war, a host of instruments of destruction which will facilitate that labor, even as they have facilitated all others.

But no scientist, no matter how aware he may be of these fruits of his science, cultivates his work, or refrains from it, because of arguments such as these. No scientist can hope to evaluate what his studies, his researches, his experiments may in the end produce for his fellow men, except in one respect—if they are sound, they will produce knowledge. And this deep complementarity between what may be conceived to be the social justification of science and what is for the individual his compelling motive in its pursuit makes us look for other answers to the question of the relation of science to society.

One of these is that the scientist should assume responsibility for the fruits of his work. I would not argue against this, but it must be clear to all of us how very modest such assumption of responsibility can be, how very ineffective it has been in the past, how necessarily ineffective it will surely be in the future. In fact, it appears little more than exhortation to the man of learning to be properly uncomfortable, and, in the worst instances, is used as a sort of screen to justify the most casual, unscholarly and, in the last analysis, corrupt intrusion of scientists into other realms of which they have neither experience nor knowledge, nor the patience to obtain them.

The true responsibility of a scientist, as we all know, is to the integrity and vigor of his science. And because most scientists, like all men of learning, tend in part also to be teachers, they have a responsibility for the communication of the truths they have found. This is at least a collective if not an individual responsibility. That we should see in this any insurance that the fruits of science will be used for man's benefit, or denied to man when they make for his distress or destruction, would be a tragic naïveté.

There is another side of the coin. This is the question of

whether there are elements in the way of life of the scientist which need not be restricted to the professional, and which have hope in them for bringing dignity and courage and serenity to other men. Science is not all of the life of reason; it is a part of it. As such, what can it mean to man?

Perhaps it would be well to emphasize that I am talking neither of wisdom nor of an elite of scientists, but precisely of the kind of work and thought, of action and discipline, that makes up the everyday professional life of the scientist. It is not of any general insight into human affairs that I am talking. It is not the kind of thing we recognize in our greatest statesmen, after long service devoted to practical affairs and to the public interest. It is something very much more homely and robust than that. It has in it the kind of beauty that is inseparable from craftsmanship and form, but it has in it also the vigor that we rightly associate with the simple, ordered lives of artisans or of farmers, that we rightly associate with lives to which limitations of scope, and traditional ways, have given robustness and structure.

Even less would it be right to interpret the question of what there is in the ways of science that may be of general value to mankind in terms of the creation of an elite. The study of physics, and I think my colleagues in the other sciences will let me speak for them too, does not make philosopher-kings. It has not, until now, made kings. It almost never makes fit philosophers—so rarely that they must be counted as exceptions. If the professional pursuit of science makes good scientists, if it makes men with a certain serenity in their lives, who yield perhaps a little more slowly than others to the natural corruptions of their time, it is doing a great deal, and all that we may rightly ask of it. For if Plato believed that in the study of geometry, a man might prepare himself for wisdom and responsibility in the world of men, it was precisely because he thought so hopefully that the understanding of men could be patterned after the understanding of geometry. If we believe that today, it is in a much more recondite sense, and a much more cautious one.

Where, then, is the point? For one thing, it is to describe some of the features of the professional life of the scientist, which make of it one of the great phenomena of the contemporary world. Here again I would like to speak of physics; but I have enough friends in the other sciences to know how close their experience is to ours. And I know too that despite profound differences in method and technique, differences which surely are an appropriate reflection of the difference in the areas of the world under study, what I would say of physics will seem familiar to workers in other disparate fields, such as mathematics or biology.

What are some of these points? There is, in the first instance, a total lack of authoritarianism, which is hard to comprehend or to admit unless one has lived with it. This is accomplished by one of the most exacting of intellectual disciplines. In physics the worker learns the possibility of error very early. He learns that there are ways to correct his mistakes; he learns the futility of trying to conceal them. For it is not a field in which error awaits death and subsequent generations for verdict—the next issue of the journals will take care of it. The refinement of techniques for the prompt discovery of error serves as well as any other as a hallmark of what we mean by science.

In any case, it is an area of collective effort in which there is a clear and well-defined community whose canons of taste and order simplify the life of the practitioner. It is a field in which the technique of experiment has given an almost perfect harmony to the balance between thought and action. In it we learn, so frequently that we could almost become accustomed to it, how vast is the novelty of the world, and how much even the physical world transcends in delicacy and in balance the limits of man's prior imaginings. We learn that views may be useful and inspiriting although they are not complete. We come to have a great caution in all assertions of totality, of finality or absoluteness.

In this field quite ordinary men, using what are in the last analysis only the tools which are generally available in our society, manage to unfold for themselves and all others who wish to learn, the rich story of one aspect of the physical world, and of man's experience. We learn to throw away those instruments of action and those modes of description which are not appropriate to the reality we are trying to discern, and in this most painful discipline, find ourselves modest before the world.

The question which is so much in our mind is whether a comparable experience, a comparable discipline, a comparable community of interest, can in any way be available to mankind at large. I suppose that all the professional scientists together number some one one-hundreth of a per cent of the men of the world—even this will define rather generously what we mean by scientists. Scientists as professionals are, I suppose, rather sure to constitute a small part of our people.

Clearly, if we raise at all this question that I have raised, it must be in the hope that there are other areas of human experience that may be discovered or invented or cultivated, and to which the qualities which distinguish scentific life may be congenial and appropriate. It is natural that serious scientists, knowing of their own experience something of the quality of their profession, should just today be concerned about its possible extension. For it is a time when the destruction and the evil of the last quarter century make men everywhere eager to seek all that can contribute to their intellectual life, some of the order and freedom and purpose which we conceive the great days of the past to have. Of all intellectual activity, science alone has flourished in the last centuries, science alone has turned out to have the kind of universality among men which the times require. I shall be disputed in this; but it is near to truth.

If one looks at past history, one may derive some encouragement for the hope that science, as one of the forms of reason, will nourish all of its forms. One may note how integral the love and cultivation of science were with the whole awakening of the human spirit which characterized the Renaissance. Or one may look at the late seventeenth and eighteenth centuries in France and England and see what pleasure and what stimulation the men of that time derived from the growth of physics, astronomy and mathematics.

What perhaps characterizes these periods of the past,

which we must be careful not to make more heroic because of their remoteness, was that there were many men who were able to combine in their own lives the activities of a scientist with activities of art and learning and politics, and were able to carry over from the one into the others this combination of courage and modesty which is the lesson that science always tries to teach to anyone who practices it.

And here we come to a point we touched earlier. It is very different to hear the results of science, as they may be descriptively or even analytically taught in a class or in a book or in the popular talk of the time; it is very different to hear these and to participate even in a modest way in the actual attainment of new knowledge. For it is just characteristic of all work in scientific fields that there is no authority to whom to refer, no one to give canon, no one to blame if the picture does not make sense.

Clearly these circumstances pose a question of great difficulty in the field of education. For if there is any truth in the views that I have outlined, there is all the difference in the world between hearing about science or its results and sharing in the experience of the scientist himself and of that of the scientific community. We all know that an awareness of this, and an awareness of the value of science as method, rather than science as doctrine, underlies the practices of teaching to scientist and layman alike. For surely the whole notion of incorporating a laboratory in a high school or college is a deference to the belief that not only what the scientist finds but how he finds it is worth learning and teaching and worth living through.

Yet there is something fake about all this. No one who has had to do with elementary instruction can have escaped a sense of artificiality in the way in which students are led, by the calculations of their instructors, to follow paths which will tell them something about the physical world. Precisely that groping for what is the appropriate experiment, what are the appropriate terms in which to view subtle or complex phenomena, which are the substance of scientific effort, almost inevitably are distilled out of it by the natural patterns of pedagogy. The teaching of science to laymen is not wholly a loss; and here perhaps physics is an atypically bad example. But surely they are rare men who, entering upon a life in which science plays no direct part, remember from their early courses in physics what science is like or what it is good for. The teaching of science is at its best when it is most like an apprenticeship.

President Conant, in his sensitive and thoughtful book *On Understanding Science*, has spoken at length of these matters. He is aware of how false it is to separate scientific theory from the groping, fumbling, tentative efforts which lead to it. He is aware that it is science as method and not as doctrine which we should try to teach. His basic suggestion is that we attempt to find, in the history of our sciences, stories which can be re-created in the instruction and experiment of the student and which thus can enable him to see at firsthand how error may give way to less error, confusion to less confusion, and bewilderment to insight.

The problem that President Conant has here presented is indeed a deep one. Yet he would be quite willing, I think, that I express skepticism that one can re-create the experience of science as an artifact. And he would no doubt share my concern that science so taught would be corrupt with antiquarianism. It was not antiquarianism but a driving curiosity that inspired in the men of the Renaissance their deep interest in classical culture.

For it is in fact difficult, almost to the point of impossibility, to re-create the climate of opinion in which substantial errors about the physical world, now no longer entertained, were not only held but were held unquestioned as part of the obvious mode of thinking about reality. It is most difficult to do because in all human thought only the tiniest fraction of our experience is in focus, and because to this focus a whole vast unanalyzed account of experience must be brought to bear. Thus I am inclined to think that, with exceptions I hope will be many but fear will be few, the attempt to give the history of science as a living history will be far more difficult than either to tell of the knowledge that we hold today or to write externally of that history as it may appear in the learned books. It could easily lead to a sort of exercise of mental inventiveness on the part of teachers and students alike which is the very opposite of the candor, the "no holds barred" rules of Professor Bridgman, that characterize scientific understanding at its best.

If I am troubled by President Conant's suggestions, this is not at all because I doubt that the suggestions he makes are desirable. I do have a deep doubt as to the extent to which they may be practical. There is something irreversible about acquiring knowledge; and the simulation of the search for it differs in a most profound way from the reality. In fact, it would seem that only those who had some firsthand experience in the acquisition of new knowledge in some disciplined field would be able truly to appreciate how great the science of the past has been, and would be able to measure those giant accomplishments against their own efforts to penetrate a few millimeters farther into darkness that surrounds them.

Thus it would seem at least doubtful that the spiritual fruits of science could be made generally available, either by the communication of its results, or by the study of its history, or by the necessarily somewhat artificial re-enactment of its procedures. Rather it would seem that there are general features of the scientists' work the direct experience of which in any context could contribute more to this end. All of us, I suppose, would list such features and find it hard to define the words which we found it necessary to use in our lists. But on a few, a common experience may enable us to talk in concert.

In the first instance the work of science is co-operative; a scientist takes his colleagues as judges, competitors and collaborators. That does not mean, of course, that he loves his colleagues; but it gives him a way of living with them which would be not without its use in the contemporary world. The work of science is discipline in that its essential inventiveness is most of all dedicated to means for promptly revealing error. One may think of the rigors of mathematics and the virtuosity of physical experiment as two examples. Science is disciplined in its rejection of questions that cannot be answered and in its grinding pursuit of methods for answering all that can. Science is always limited, and is in a profound sense unmetaphysical, in that it necessarily bases itself upon the broad ground of common human experience, tries to refine it within narrow areas where progress seems possible and exploration fruitful. Science is novelty and change. When it closes it dies. These qualities constitute a way of life which of course does not make wise men from foolish, or good men from wicked, but which has its beauty and which seems singularly suited to man's estate on earth.

If there is to be any advocacy at all in this talk, it would be this: that we be very sensitive to all new possibilities of extending the techniques and the patterns of science into other areas of human experience. Even in saying this we must be aware how slow the past development of science has in fact been, how much error there has been, and how much in it that turned out to be contrary to intellectual health or honesty.

We become fully aware of the need for caution if we look for a moment at what are called the social problems of the day and try to think what one could mean by approaching them in the scientific spirit, of trying to give substance, for example, to the feeling that a society that could develop atomic energy could also develop the means of controlling it. Surely the establishment of a secure peace is very much in all our minds. It is right that we try to bring reason to bear on an understanding of this problem; but for that there are available to us no equivalents of the experimental techniques of science. Errors of conception can remain undetected and even undefined. No means of appropriately narrowing the focus of thinking is known to us. Nor have we found good avenues for extending or deepening our experience that bears upon this problem. In short, almost all the preconditions of scientific activity are missing, and in this case, at least, one may have a melancholy certainty that man's inventiveness will not rapidly provide them. All that we have from science in facing such great questions is a memory of our professional life, which makes us somewhat skeptical of other people's assertions, somewhat critical of enthusiasms so difficult to define and to control.

Yet the past century has seen many valid and inspiriting examples for the extension of science to new domains. As even in the case of physics, the initial steps are always controversial; probably we should not as a group be unanimous in saying which of these extensions were hopeful, and which not, for the science of the future. But one feature which I cannot fail to regard as sound—particularly in the fields of biology and psychology—is that they provide an appropriate means of correlating understanding and action, and involve new experimental procedures in terms of which a new conceptual apparatus can be defined; above all, they give us means of detecting error. In fact, one of the features which must arouse our suspicion of the dogmas some of Freud's followers have built up on the initial brilliant works of Freud is the tendency toward a self-sealing system, a system, that is, which has a way of almost automatically discounting evidence which might bear adversely on the doctrine. The whole point of science is to do just the opposite: to invite the detection of error and to welcome it. Some of you may think that in another field a comparable system has been developed by the recent followers of Marx.

Thus we may hope for an ever-widening and more diverse field of application of science. But we must be aware how slowly these things develop and how little their development is responsive to even the most desperate of man's needs. For me it is an open question, and yet not a trivial one, whether in a time necessarily limited by the threats of war and of chaos these expanding areas in which the scientific spirit can flourish may yet contribute in a decisive way to man's rational life.

I have had to leave this essential question unanswered: I am not at all proud of that. In lieu of apology perhaps I may tell a story of another lecturer, speaking at Harvard, a few miles from here, two decades ago. Bertrand Russell had given a talk on the then new quantum mechanics, of whose wonders he was most appreciative. He spoke hard and earnestly in the New Lecture Hall. And when he was done, Professor Whitehead, who presided, thanked him for his efforts, and not least for "leaving the vast darkness of the subject unobscured."

VI

The Encouragement of Science

THIS WAS *an address made in Washington, D. C., on March 7, 1950, to the winners of the annual Westinghouse Science Talent Search. These were high-school students who had shown talent in science and who were given awards to assist them in further study.*

VI

The Encouragement of Science

WE ARE here tonight to honor you and to celebrate the high promise of your future as scientists. We are happy to be with you. We think of that future with respect and curiosity. We think of the discoveries which you will make. We think of the questions to which we today have no answer and to which you will come to know an answer. Even more, we think of the answers that we have today and of the new questions that you will put to those answers. We think of how altered and how deepened our knowledge of the world will be before you are through with it. My first wish to you is that you may make and that you may share in the making of great and beautiful discoveries which enrich our knowledge of the world of nature and of man. I have a second wish for you; but that must come at the end of my talk.

I do not propose to talk to you of such topics of the day as the hydrogen bomb and the statutory provisions of the National Science Foundation. If these matters are not in a very different state when you shall have come to assume the full responsibilities of citizenship, you will have reason to reproach your elders for your inheritance.

Science has profoundly altered the conditions of man's life. During the last centuries, the discoveries in science and their applications to practice have changed the material conditions of life. They have changed as well many matters of the spirit. They have changed the form in which practical problems of right and wrong come before us; they have changed the focus of moral issues, both for the individual and for governments. They have given us new methods for defining the meaning of problems that face us and for judging whether or not our solutions are just.

The most manifest of the changes are the material ones. Yet even here it takes a certain perspective to see their true extent. Advances in the study of man and other living forms have extended our life span by decades. Discoveries in physical science have immeasurably lightened our toil and enriched our lives. They have given leisure to an ever-widening group of men. They have made a reasonable education not a special privilege but a common right. They have made the world, in its physical dimensions, a small place, and established the means by which people in remote parts of the earth can communicate with each other, can get to know each other, and can learn to work together. They have put at the disposal of everyone the resources of physical power, of ease and of knowledge that were in the past reserved for the few.

Not all the changes in material well-being that science offers are realities. Yet the very fact that they are possibilities has changed the nature of the responsibility which we bear, both as individuals and as a community of men and women banded together in government. In the Greek cities, political democracy and civilization itself appeared possible only on the basis of a slave economy. Technology, born of science, has altered that; it has enabled mankind, as it has forced mankind, to deal with the issues of slavery as a moral issue. Poverty has always been an ugly thing, and in its extremes a desperate one. Today it is an evil, in the sense that it lies within human hands and human hearts to abate it. Science can provide us, for the first time in history, with the means of abating hunger for everyone on earth.

Perhaps nowhere has the impact of science more clearly altered the specific terms of a great political issue than in the effects of scientific development on warfare. This is a can of worms with which I have myself unhappily been engaged for some years. It would not be honest to say—as it would be folly not to hope—that the very terror of modern weapons would in itself put an end to war; it would not even be honest to say that because of this terror the abolition of war and the maintenance of peace have become the one absolute, final objective of all political decisions. There are other things in man's life—his freedom, his decency, his sense of right and wrong—that cannot so lightly be subjected to a single end. But what we need to remember is that war today has become, and is increasingly becoming, something very different from what it was a century ago or a millennium ago. We need to recognize the new situation as new; we need to come to it with something of the same spirit as the scientist's when he has conducted an experiment and finds that the results are totally other than those that he had anticipated.

Four months before Hiroshima, in the last days of his life, President Roosevelt's thoughts turned to these questions. In the last words that he wrote, in words he did not live to speak, the President looked to the future, to the atomic age. He looked to the past, to the days of the founding of the Republic. He wrote:

"Thomas Jefferson, himself a distinguished scientist, once spoke of the 'brotherly spirit of science, which unites into one family all its votaries of whatever grade, and however widely dispersed throughout the different quarters of the globe.'

"Today science has brought all the different quarters of the globe so close together that it is impossible to isolate them one from another.

"Today we are faced with the pre-eminent fact that, if civilization is to survive, we must cultivate the science of human relationships—the ability of all peoples, of all kinds, to live together and work together, in the same world, at peace."

Science has greatly extended the range of questions in

which man has a choice; it has extended man's freedom to make significant decisions. Is there anything in the methods of science itself, or in the spirit of science, which can help in the making of these decisions? To what extent is there a play on the word *science* which can mislead us and take us up false roads when we speak of this science of human relationships? Is there anything we can learn from the relevance of science to politics?

If we are to answer these questions and answer them honestly, we must recognize important and basic differences between problems of science and problems of action as they arise in personal or in political life. If we fail to recognize these differences, we shall be seeking magic solutions and not real ones. We shall delude ourselves into laying aside responsibility, which it is an essential part of man's life to bear.

In most scientific study, questions of good and evil or right and wrong play at most a minor and secondary part. For practical decisions of policy, they are basic. Without them political action would be meaningless. Practical decisions and, above all, political decisions can never quite be freed from the conflicting claims of special interest. These too are part of the meaning of a decision and of a course of action, and they must be an essential part of the force of its implementation.

Political decisions are unique acts. In politics there is little that can correspond to the scientist's repetition of an experiment. An experiment that fails in its purpose may be as good or better than one that succeeds, because it may well be more instructive. A political decision cannot be taken twice. All the factors that are relevant to it will conjoin only once. The analogies of history can provide a guide, but only a very partial one.

These are formidable differences between the problems of science and those of practice. They show that the method of science cannot be directly adapted to the solution of problems in politics and in man's spiritual life. Yet there is relevance of a more subtle but by no means trivial kind.

In trying more fully to explore this relevance, I should like to start with a text. This text is a letter* written by Thomas Jefferson to a young man who had inquired of him as to the usefulness of his studies of science. It was written in the middle of the year 1799, the year in which Napoleon abolished the Directory and began to assume dictatorial power in France, the year before Thomas Jefferson was elected for the first time as President of the United States. Jefferson and the diverse brave and hopeful men who with him laid the foundations of our own government had learned much from the peoples of other nations. Many of their highest political ideals and their most powerful political instruments were built on the experience, the insight and wisdom of European scientists and philosophers. Even today we need to remember that this was so, that there may be much we can learn from others, and that we should be glad to learn, as in turn by example we should be glad to teach.

Jefferson's letter starts with a survey of the subjects in science which he believes young Munford ought to pursue.

* *Scripta Mathematica* I, 1932, 88-92.

I will quote one characteristic passage which may strike a familiar and homely note for you:

". . . the science of calculation also is indispensible as far as the extraction of the square and cube roots; Algebra as far as the quadratic equation and the use of logarithms are often of value in ordinary cases: but all beyond these is but a luxury; a delicious luxury indeed; but not to be indulged in by one who is to have a profession to follow for his subsistence."

But that is not really the part of Jefferson's letter which I commend to you. Here it is:

"I am among those who think well of the human character generally. I consider man as formed for society, and endowed by nature with those dispositions which fit him for society. I believe also, with Condorcet, as mentioned in your letter, that his mind is perfectible to a degree of which we cannot as yet form any conception. It is impossible for a man who takes a survey of what is already known, not to see what an immensity in every branch of science yet remains to be discovered, and that too of articles to which our faculties seem adequate."

And later, in the same letter, still more explicitly:

". . . and it is still more certain that in the other branches of science, great fields are yet to be explored to which our faculties are equal, and that to an extent of which we cannot fix the limits. I join you therefore in branding as cowardly the idea that the human mind is incapable of further advances. This is precisely the doctrine which the present despots of the earth are inculcating, and their friends here re-echoing; and applying especially to religion and politics; 'that it is not probable that any thing better will be discovered than what was known to our fathers.' We are to look backwards then and not forwards for the improvement of science, and to find it amidst feudal barbarisms and the fires of Spital-fields. But thank heaven the American mind is already too much opened, to listen to these impostures; and while the art of printing is left to us, science can never be retrograde; what is once acquired of real knowledge can never be lost. To preserve the freedom of the human mind then and freedom of the press, every spirit should be ready to devote itself to martyrdom; for as long as we may think as we will, and speak as we think, the condition of man will proceed in improvement. The generation which is going off the stage has deserved well of mankind for the struggles it has made, and for having arrested that course of despotism which had overwhelmed the world for thousands and thousands of years. If there seems to be danger that the ground they have gained will be lost again, that danger comes from the generation your cotemporary. But that the enthusiasm which characterises youth should lift it's parracide hands against freedom and science would be such a monstrous phaenomenon as I cannot place among possible things in this age and this country."

To me there are two striking impressions which this letter of Jefferson's makes, even beyond its eloquence and its beauty. The first is that the letter is pervaded with the idea of progress, that ideal that owes so much to the development of science and that in turn has provided the great enriching human faith in which scientific discovery and invention have flourished. Jefferson is confident that an increased understanding of the world will lead to progress; he is convinced that the barbarisms of the past cannot stand up against inquiry and understanding and enlightenment; he is confident in man and sure that as men know more they will act more wisely and live better. In our contemporary expressions of hope that catastrophe can be averted and civilization yet be saved, that confidence has lost much of its robustness.

The second point is that for Jefferson there is something in the ways of science that is relevant to political life. Even in religion and politics, he holds that it is probable that things better will be discovered than what was known to our fathers. This conviction that new knowledge is possible, and that not all the answers are known, is of course the stuff of the day-to-day life of the scientist. Science itself does progress; new knowledge is possible; and new knowledge, because it does not destroy or ignore the old, can only increase our understanding. The very idea of the development of science is an example of progress, and of progress which in no true sense can ever be reversed. But this is only part of the story. It is true, as Jefferson knew, that in the large, science has flourished in conditions of human freedom, and that its growth is parallel to the growth of democratic institutions. Today, looking back on more than a century and a half of further history, we can be even more sure of this. We have seen not only the inspiring example of science and democracy flourishing together, but the tragic examples of their foundering together. We express the hope that of this tragedy we shall soon have seen the end.

What are these lessons that the spirit of science teaches us for our practical affairs? Basic to them all is that there may be no barriers to freedom of inquiry. Basic to them all is the ideal of openmindedness with regard to new knowledge, new experience and new truth. Science is not based on authority. It owes its acceptance and its universality to an appeal to intelligible, communicable evidence that any interested man can evaluate.

There is no place for dogma in science. The scientist is free to ask any question, to doubt any assertion, to seek for any evidence, to correct any error. Where science has been used in the past to erect a new dogmatism, that dogmatism has found itself incompatible with the progress of science; and in the end, the dogma has yielded, or science and freedom have perished together.

Our own political life is predicated on opennness. We do not believe any group of men adequate enough or wise enough to operate without scrutiny or without criticism. We know that the only way to avoid error is to detect it, that the only way to detect it is to be free to inquire. We know that the wages of secrecy are corruption. We know that in secrecy error, undetected, will flourish and subvert.

Let me be clear. Science is not skepticism. It is not the practice of science to look for things to doubt. It was not by a deliberate attempt of skepticism that physicists were led to doubt the absolute nature of simultaneity, or to recognize that the ideas of strict causality embodied in classical physics could not be applied in the domain of atomic phenomena. There is probably no group of men who take more for granted in their daily work than the scientists. Common sense and all that flows from it are their principal basis for what they do in the laboratory and for what they make of it on paper. But for scientists it is not only honorable to doubt; it is mandatory to do that when there appears to be evidence in support of the doubt. In place of authority in science we have and we need to have only the consensus of informed opinion, only the guide of example. No scientist needs to order his colleagues to use a new technique of experiment or to enter a new field of discovery. If he has done this, it will be an invitation to his fellows to follow.

These, then, are some of the attitudes of mind, these are some of the disciplines of spirit which grow naturally in the scientist's world. They have grown there in part as a result of a humane and liberal tradition in political life and in part as a cause of that. The open mind, the reliance on example and persuasion rather than on authority—these are the heritage of the centuries in which science has altered the face of the earth. Science can help in diverse ways in preserving and extending this heritage. Its very universality speaks across frontiers to make truth manifest in lands otherwise darkened; its material applications create the preconditions—in leisure, in education, in means of communication—for the converse of men with one another. Science provides the material and the intellectual basis for a world in which example and understanding can help all men to improve their lot and fulfill their hopes. Today we need to remember that our country, founded on these practices and grown strong by their exercise, owes its strength to them. In this time of crisis, we need to cherish that strength.

And this brings me to my second wish for you. I wish you not only the joy of great discovery; I wish for you a world of confidence in man and man's humanity, a world of confidence in reason, so that as you work you may be inspired by the hope that what you find will make men freer and better—in which, working as specialists in what may be recondite parts of the intellectual life of the time, you are nevertheless contributing in a direct and basic way to the welfare of mankind.

VII

The Scientist in Society

THIS TALK *was given on January 1, 1953, to a meeting of the Association of Princeton Graduate Alumni at Princeton, New Jersey.*

VII

The Scientist in Society

THERE IS something inherently comforting about a panel of experts. One knows that the partial and inadequate and slanted and personal views that he expresses will be corrected by the less partial, less personal views of everyone else on the panel; it is not unlike the experience of the professor who always is glad that he has to meet his class again because he can correct the mistakes that he made the last time. It is with such tentativeness that I am going to talk to you.

This is a vast terrain—one full of strange precipices,

chasms and terrors. What I thought I would do first is to run over in a quite synoptic way a few general opinions, almost words only, which seem to me involved in the relations between science and man's life. It is my hope that I will do this with enough baldness so that you will pick up some of these words and deal with them more fully and more wisely than in this summary. I will then devote a little time to one problem which seems to me singularly fit in this hall and in this company, which worries me a great deal, and as to a resolution for which I have only the most rudimentary notions.

For one thing, we have changed the face of the earth; we have changed the way men live. We may not change the condition of man's life, but we have changed all modes in which that condition occurs. I do not by this mean to say that from the existence of science, from the discovery, knowledge, technique and power of science the particularities of the present time follow. But we all know that if life today is very different from what it was two hundred years ago, if we meet our human and political problems in a quite new form, that has much to do with the fact that we know how to do a great many things, and that there are people who are eager to do them, not typically scientists, but people who are glad to use the knowledge and with it the control which science has made available.

I need not belittle two points. One is that the effect of science on the condition of man's life is also in part a cultural and intellectual one. I shall return to that because it is my persuasion that this is largely a happy symbiosis of the past; today we have very little of it. The ideas which have changed the thinking caps of men and which derived from experience in science are really not contemporary ideas but go back a century or two centuries or more.

The second, of course, is not to try to give to scientific life an autonomy of society. It is possible, manifestly, for society so to arrange things that there is no science. The Nazis made a good start in that direction; maybe the Communists will achieve it; and there is not one of us free of the worry that this flourishing tree may someday not be alive any more.

But nonetheless we *have* changed the face of the earth; any beginning of a talk about science and society must take that as a fact.

There is another theme. This is a time that tends to believe in progress. Our ways of thought, our ways of arranging our personal lives, our political forms, point to the future, point not merely to change, to decay, to alteration, but point with a hopeful note of improvement that our progress is inevitable. In the acquisition of knowledge, in the very notion of a cumulative discipline, tomorrow in a certain sense comprises today and yesterday. How much this built-in sense of progress in man's life—which is, I think, not a religious notion, not a Christian notion—how much this derives from the effects of science on philosophical and political thought I would leave to historians of ideas. It is probably not wholly trivial.

A third theme is that science in a certain sense is universal. It is not universal in the sense that all men participate in it. It is universal in the sense that all men can participate in it. It is nonnational, nonlocal and, although one would not say noncultural, singularly independent of the form of government, the immediate tradition, or the affective life of a people. It has to do with *humanitas*. This universality is not a trivial thing at a time when forms of unity, large forms of unity in the world, appear to be for other reasons rather necessary. This has been very much in all our minds in the years since the last war. I remember that on one occasion when I was in this hall, at the Bicentennial of the University, we were talking about the universality of science; and at that very moment the Soviet delegate to the United Nations Atomic Energy Commission was imploring his government for permission to accept the scientific and technical report of the subcommittee of this commission. This, I think, is the last time—the last time I remember—that the Soviet government has said *yes* to anything, has said *yes* to an agreement of fact. I know how bitterly disappointing the experiences of these years have been as to universality of science, but we all know that this is bad politics but not bad science. We all know that there is no such thing as German physics or Soviet genetics or American astronomy. These fields can open themselves to all reasonable men willing to take the trouble to inquire.

There is also what may first seem like the opposite of universality; I hope you will bear that in mind when I talk of science as a great and beautiful word. There *is* a unity to it; but there is also an even more striking and immense diversity. Both of your speakers this morning are physicists, and I think we are very different from our brothers the chemists and our brothers the mathematicians. In our values, in our style, we are different. Physics is perhaps the branch of science which has been most concerned to keep itself one. The Physical Society splits off divisions from time to time but is reluctant to do so; and the divisions largely have to do with semi-applied science. Physics has a history of close association with mathematics, with astronomy, with epistemology and cosmology too. And yet we do not know very much about the rest of the scientists. I know that it is a very happy occasion at the Institute when some piece of work turns up which is of interest to both the mathematicians and the physicists. It is a very rare occasion and we tend to ring bells when a small bit of cement can be found between their interests. I would stress especially that there is no systematic unity of techniques, of appreciation, of values, of style between the many things that we call science. There is a lot of difference between the nuclear physicist and the agricultural scientist exploring the possibility of improving crops in some poor island in the Caribbean. They are scientists, and they understand each other, and we hope love each other. But they are not very much alike.

There are perhaps two or three other general things. One I believe may be of more importance to some of the other panels than to this. This is one of the by-products of the great flowering of science that dates back to the time when science did have an effect on culture and on ideas. We have been impressed, and I must say I never stop being impressed, by the great sweep of general order in which particulars are recognized as united. You know the examples: electricity and light, the quantum theory and the theory of valence, places where things that appeared to be separate, and each having its own order, appear as illustrations of a more general order. And one may say, I suppose, that science is a search for regularity and order in those domains of experience which have proven accessible to it.

I am not sure that the effect of the impressive victory of man's mind in this enterprise has not been to make us a little obtuse to the role of the contingent and the particular in life. It is true that many particulars can be understood and subsumed by a general order. But it is probably no less a great truth that elements of abstractly irreconcilable general orders can be subsumed by a particular. And this notion might be more useful to our friends who study man and his life than an insistence on following the lines which in natural science have been so overwhemingly successful.

There is another great complex of questions. These I feel reassured to mention hardly at all because my friend and successor Dr. Waterman has thought so deeply about them; he is perhaps as well informed as any man in the world. This has to do with the great variety of means whereby society patronizes science, whereby it is possible for the scientist to operate and live and eat and do his work, get in some sense a bit of encouragement and in some sense a bit of nourishment. The problem of patronage is a complex one; it is changing; it has changed enormously in the last decade in this country. I leave it with a good conscience to Alan Waterman that he may deal with it wisely.

What is it, then, that bothers me especially, that I want not merely to mention but to worry about here? I think that in this matter perhaps this panel is not so different than the panel on the role of the artist, or the panel on the role of the philosopher. To put it with great brutality, the point is that the scientist is not in society today, any more than is the artist or the philosopher.

Of course, he does get paid, he does get patronized and even, for odd reasons that he sometimes does not understand, respected. But he is not in society, in the sense that the ideas he has, the work he is doing, stop really rather short with the limits of his profession. They are not part of the intellectual and cultural life of the times. I am over and over again appalled by how ignorant, how incredibly ignorant of the most rudimentary things about my subject are my fellows the historians, my acquaintances the statesmen, my friends the men of affairs. They have no notion of what cooks in physics; I think that they have very little notion of what cooks in any other science. And I know that only by good luck and some hard work do I have even a rudimentary notion of what cooks in other parts of the house called science than the one that I live in. I read the *Physical Review* and work very hard to catch up with it every two weeks; and I think maybe I have some notion of what is going on in some parts of physics; but by and large we know little about one another, and the world outside knows nothing about us. I think this may vary a little from place to place. Perhaps it is tradition in Britain, where there is a sort of deliberate tendency, a national tendency, to refuse to let things become obscure and recondite, that there is a little more effort to see that civilized men have a notion of what the mathematicians and astronomers and physicists are doing—not merely to know the by-products of their works, the practical products, but what they are thinking.

This is in very sharp contrast, this startling general ignorance of scientific ideas and discoveries at the edge of the technical disciplines, in very sharp contrast to the state of affairs two or three centuries ago; and some of the reasons for this are manifest. But I believe that the science of today is subtler, richer, more relevant to man's life and more useful to man's dignity than the science which had such a great effect on the age of the enlightenment, had such a great effect, among other things, on the forms and patterns, traditions and hopes—reflected in our Constitution—of human society. Science is not retrograde; and there is no doubt that the quantum mechanics represents a more interesting, more instructive, richer analogy of human life than Newtonian mechanics could conceivably be. There is no doubt that even the theory of relativity, which has been so much vulgarized and so little understood, that even the theory of relativity is a matter which would be of real interest to people at large. There is no doubt that the findings of biology and astronomy and chemistry are discoveries that would enrich our whole culture if they were understood. And what is perhaps more troublesome, there is a gulf between the life of the scientist and the life of a man who isn't actively a scientist, dangerously deep. The experience of science—to stub your toe hard and then notice that it was really a rock on which you stubbed it—this experience is something that is hard to communicate by popularization, by education, or by talk. It is almost as hard to tell a man what it is like to find out something new about the world as it is to describe a mystical experience to a chap who has never had any hint of such an experience.

The enlightenment was a peculiar time; it was hopeful, and superficial, and humane; and how much of the ideas of the enlightenment derived from an appreciation of science, it is perhaps not right for anyone but a careful historian to say. But we know that the same men who wrote about politics and philosophy—not very good philosophy, and not too good politics—also wrote about natural science, about physics, and astronomy, and mathematics. We know that on two very different planes Franklin and Jefferson managed to span the whole way from a living, and in some cases even practicing, interest in science to the world of affairs. And we know how full their writings are of the illumination which one sheds on the other.

Science in those days was connected with the practical arts; it was very close to common sense. Yet always there is in science little more than the infinitely diligent and patient and unremitting application of the practical arts and common sense. By now it has come to be a long chain. The mere process of carrying a boy through the elementary steps of this chain consumes so much of his life and is such an exhausting operation, to the teacher and student alike, that the simple means of communication and understanding, which sufficed in the seventeenth and eighteenth centuries, are clearly not good enough.

This is a problem that has had the thought of many wise people; I do not pretend to be talking of anything new or strange. I suppose the notion of having laboratory courses was an attempt to bring the young man and woman into this experience of really discovering something; yet my fear is that by the time it gets into the laboratory and the professor knows the answer, the whole operation is different; it is an imitation and not the real thing. I suppose all of you have read the eloquent pleas which a number of scientists, of whom perhaps President Conant is the best known, have made for attempting to communicate some understanding of science by what is essentially the historical method. These do, I think, establish the fact that science as a human activity is treatable by the historical method. They do not, I think, establish that a scientific method, or a scientific discovery, is communicable by these means. I have a great anxiety that our educational directions, far from making us a part of the world we live in, in this very special sense that we share ideas and some bit of experience with our fellow men, may even be moving rather in the opposite direction.

This is odd: we live in the world very much affected by science, and even our thinking caps, and our ideas and the terms in which we tend to talk about things, the notion of progress, the notion of a fraternity of scholars and scientists which is so familiar to a Christian life and which has a new twist because of the spread of science—all of these we can see originally at a time when science was understood by men of affairs, by artists, by poets. We live today in a world in which poets and historians and men of affairs are proud that they wouldn't even begin to consider thinking about learning anything of science, regarding it as the far end of a tunnel too long for any wise man to put his head into. We therefore have, in so far as we have at all, a philosophy that is quite anachronistic and, I am convinced, quite inadequate to our times. I think that whatever may have been thought of Cartesian and Newtonian reforms in the intellectual life of Europe, the time when these were what the doctor ordered—all that the doctor ordered—is long past. Far more subtle recognition of the nature of man's knowledge and of his relations to the universe is certainly long overdue, if we are to do justice to the wisdom which our tradition has in it and to the brilliant and ever-changing flower of discovery which is modern science.

Research is action; and the question I want to leave in a very raw and uncomfortable form with you is how to communicate this sense of action to our fellow men who are not destined to devote their lives to the professional pursuit of new knowledge.

VIII

Prospects in the Arts and Sciences

THIS WAS *the concluding lecture in a series dedicated to "Man's Right to Knowledge and the Free Use Thereof" which was part of the celebration of Columbia University's Bicentennial. The talk was recorded in November 1954, and first broadcast by the Columbia Broadcasting System on December 26, 1954.*

VIII

Prospects in the Arts and Sciences

THE WORDS "prospects in the arts and sciences" mean two quite different things to me. One is prophecy: What will the scientists discover and the painters paint, what new forms will alter music, what parts of experience will newly yield to objective description? The other meaning is that of a view: What do we see when we look at the world today and compare it with the past? I am not a prophet; and I cannot very well speak to the first subject, though in many ways I should like to. I shall try to speak to the second, because there are some features of this view which seem to me so remarkable, so new and so arresting, that it may be worth turning our eyes to them; it may even help us to create and shape the future better, though we cannot foretell it.

In the arts and in the sciences, it would be good to be a prophet. It would be a delight to know the future. I had thought for a while of my own field of physics and of those nearest to it in the natural sciences. It would not be too hard to outline the questions which natural scientists today are asking themselves and trying to answer. What, we ask in physics, is matter, what is it made of, how does it behave when it is more and more violently atomized, when we try to pound out of the stuff around us the ingredients which only violence creates and makes manifest? What, the chemists ask, are those special features of nucleic acids and proteins which make life possible and give it its characteristic endurance and mutability? What subtle chemistry, what arrangements, what reactions and controls make the cells of living organisms differentiate so that they may perform functions as oddly diverse as transmitting information throughout our nervous systems or covering our heads with hair? What happens in the brain to make a record of the past, to hide it from consciousness, to make it accessible to recall? What are the physical features which make consciousness possible?

All history teaches us that these questions that we think the pressing ones will be transmuted before they are answered, that they will be replaced by others, and that the very process of discovery will shatter the concepts that we today use to describe our puzzlement.

It is true that there are some who profess to see in matters of culture, in matters precisely of the arts and sciences, a certain macrohistorical pattern, a grand system of laws which determines the course of civilization and gives a kind of inevitable quality to the unfolding of the future. They would, for instance, see the radical, formal experimentation which characterized the music of the last half-century as an inevitable consequence of the immense flowering and enrichment of natural science; they would see a necessary order in the fact that innovation in music precedes that in painting and that in turn in poetry, and point to this sequence in older cultures. They would attribute the formal experimentation of the arts to the dissolution, in an industrial and technical society, of authority—of secular, political authority, and of the catholic authority of the church. They are thus armed to predict the future. But this, I fear, is not my dish.

If a prospect is not a prophecy, it is a view. What does the world of the arts and sciences look like? There are two ways of looking at it: One is the view of the traveler, going by horse or foot, from village to village to town, staying in each to talk with those who live there and to gather something of the quality of its life. This is the intimate view, partial, somewhat accidental, limited by the limited life and strength and curiosity of the traveler, but intimate and human, in a human compass. The other is the vast view, showing the earth with its fields and towns and valleys as they appear to a camera carried in a high-altitude rocket. In one sense this prospect will be more complete; one will see all branches of knowledge, one will see all the arts, one will see them as part of the vastness and complication of the whole of human life on earth. But one will miss a great deal; the beauty and warmth of human life will largely be gone from that prospect.

It is in this vast high-altitude survey that one sees the general surprising quantitative features that distinguish our time. This is where the listings of science and endowments and laboratories and books published show up; this is where we learn that more people are engaged in scientific research today than ever before, that the Soviet world and the free world are running neck and neck in the training of scientists, that more books are published per capita in England than in the United States, that the social sciences are pursued actively in America, Scandinavia, and England, that there are more people who hear the great music of the past, and more music composed and more paintings painted. This is where we learn that the arts and sciences are flourishing. This great map, showing the world from afar and almost as to a stranger, would show more: It would show the immense diversity of culture and life, diversity in place and tradition for the first time clearly manifest on a world-wide scale, diversity in technique and language, separating science from science and art from art, and all of one from all of the other. This great map, world-wide, culture-wide, remote, has some odd features. There are innumerable villages. Between the villages there appear to be almost no paths discernible from this high altitude. Here and there passing near a village, sometimes through its heart, there will be a superhighway, along which windy traffic moves at enormous speed. The superhighways seem to have little connection with villages, starting anywhere, ending anywhere, and sometimes appearing almost by design to disrupt the quiet of the village. This view gives us no sense of order or of unity. To find these we must visit the villages, the quiet, busy places, the laboratories and studies and studios. We must see the paths that are barely discernible; we must understand the superhighways and their dangers.

In the natural sciences these are and have been and are likely to continue to be heroic days. Discovery follows discovery, each both raising and answering questions, each ending a long search, and each providing the new instruments for a new search. There are radical ways of thinking unfamiliar to common sense and connected with it by decades or centuries of increasingly specialized and unfamiliar experience. There are lessons of how limited, for all its variety, the common experience of man has been with regard to natural phenomena, and hints and analogies as to how limited may be his experience with man. Every new finding is a part of the instrument kit of the sciences for further investigation and for penetrating into new fields. Discoveries of knowledge fructify technology and the practical arts, and these in turn pay back refined techniques, new possibilities of observation and experiment.

In any science there is harmony between practitioners. A man may work as an individual, learning of what his colleagues do through reading or conversation; he may be working as a member of a group on problems whose technical equipment is too massive for individual effort. But whether he is a part of a team or solitary in his own study, he, as a professional, is a member of a community. His colleagues in his own branch of science will be grateful to him for the inventive or creative thoughts he has, will welcome his criticism. His world and work will be objectively communicable; and he will be quite sure that if there is error in it, that error will not long be undetected. In his own line of work he lives in a community where common understanding combines with common purpose and interest to bind men together both in freedom and in co-operation.

This experience will make him acutely aware of how limited, how inadequate, how precious is this condition of his life; for in his relations with a wider society, there will be neither the sense of community nor of objective understanding. He will sometimes find, in returning to practical undertakings, some sense of community with men who are not expert in his science, with other scientists whose work is remote from his, and with men of action and men of art. The frontiers of science are separated now by long years of study, by specialized vocabularies, arts, techniques, and knowledge from the common heritage even of a most civilized society; and anyone working at the frontier of such science is in that sense a very long way from home, a long way too from the practical arts that were its matrix and origin, as indeed they were of what we today call art.

The specialization of science is an inevitable accompaniment of progress; yet it is full of dangers, and it is cruelly wasteful, since so much that is beautiful and enlightening is cut off from most of the world. Thus it is proper to the role of the scientist that he not merely find new truth and communicate it to his fellows, but that he teach, that he try to bring the most honest and intelligible account of new knowledge to all who will try to learn. This is one reason—it is the decisive organic reason—why scientists belong in universities. It is one reason why the patronage of science by and through universities is its most proper form; for it is here, in teaching, in the association of scholars and in the friendships of teachers and taught, of men who by profession must themselves be both teachers and taught, that the narrowness of scientific life can best be moderated, and that the analogies, insights, and harmonies of scientific discovery can find their way into the wider life of man.

In the situation of the artist today there are both analogies to and differences from that of the scientist; but it is the differences which are the most striking and which raise the problems that touch most on the evil of our day. For the artist it is not enough that he communicate with others who are expert in his own art. Their fellowship, their understanding, and their appreciation may encourage him; but that is not the end of his work, nor its nature. The artist depends on a common sensibility and culture, on a common meaning of symbols, on a community of experience and common ways of describing and interpreting it. He need not write for everyone or paint or play for everyone. But his audience must be man; it must be man, and not a specialized set of experts among his fellows. Today that is very difficult. Often the artist has an aching sense of great loneliness, for the community to which he addresses himself is largely not there; the traditions and the culture, the symbols and the history, the myths and the common experience, which it is his function to illuminate, to harmonize, and to portray, have been dissolved in a changing world.

There is, it is true, an artificial audience maintained to moderate between the artist and the world for which he works: the audience of the professional critics, popularizers, and advertisers of art. But though, as does the popularizer and promoter of science, the critic fulfills a necessary present function and introduces some order and some communication between the artist and the world, he cannot add to the intimacy and the directness and the depth with which the artist addresses his fellow men.

To the artist's loneliness there is a complementary great and terrible barrenness in the lives of men. They are deprived of the illumination, the light and tenderness and insight of an intelligible interpretation, in contemporary terms, of the sorrows and wonders and gaieties and follies of man's life. This may be in part offset, and is, by the great growth of technical means for making the art of the past available. But these provide a record of past intimacies between art and life; even when they are applied to the writing and painting and composing of the day, they do not bridge the gulf between a society, too vast and too disordered, and the artist trying to give meaning and beauty to its parts.

In an important sense this world of ours is a new world, in which the unity of knowledge, the nature of human communities, the order of society, the order of ideas, the very notions of society and culture have changed and will not return to what they have been in the past. What is new is new not because it has never been there before, but because it has changed in quality. One thing that is new is the prevalence of newness, the changing scale and scope of change itself, so that the world alters as we walk in it, so that the years of man's life measure not some small growth or rearrangement or moderation of what he learned in childhood, but a great upheaval. What is new is that in one generation our knowledge of the natural world engulfs, upsets, and complements all knowledge of the natural world before. The techniques, among which and by which we live, multiply and ramify, so that the whole world is bound together by communication, blocked here and there by the immense synapses of political tyranny. The global quality of the world is new: our knowledge of and sympathy with remote and diverse peoples, our involvement with them in practical terms, and our commitment to them in terms of brotherhood. What is new in the world is the massive character of the dissolution and corruption of authority, in belief, in ritual, and in temporal order. Yet this is the world that we have come to live in. The very difficulties which it presents derive from growth in understanding, in skill, in power. To assail the changes that have unmoored us from the past is futile, and in a deep sense, I think, it is wicked. We need to recognize the change and learn what resources we have.

Again I will turn to the schools and, as their end and as their center, the universities. For the problem of the scientist is in this respect not different from that of the artist or of the historian. He needs to be a part of the community, and the community can only with loss and peril be without him. Thus it is with a sense of interest and hope that we see a growing recognition that the creative artist is a proper charge on the university, and the university a proper home for him; that a composer or a poet or a playwright or painter needs the toleration, understanding, the rather local and parochial patronage that a university can give; and that this will protect him from the tyranny of man's communication and professional promotion. For here there is an honest chance that what the artist has of insight and of beauty will take root in the community, and that some intimacy and some human bonds can mark his relations with his patrons. For a university rightly and inherently is a place where the individual man can form new syntheses, where the accidents of friendship and association can open a man's eyes to a part of science or art which he had not known before, where parts of human life, remote and perhaps superficially incompatible, can find in men their harmony and their synthesis.

These, then, in rough and far too general words, are some of the things we see as we walk through the villages of the arts and of the sciences and notice how thin are the paths that lead from one to another, and how little in terms of human understanding and pleasure the work of the villages comes to be shared outside.

The superhighways do not help. They are the mass media —from the loud-speakers in the deserts of Asia Minor and the cities of Communist China to the organized professional theater of Broadway. They are the purveyors of art and science and culture for the millions upon millions—the promoters who represent the arts and sciences to humanity and who represent humanity to the arts and sciences; they are the means by which we are reminded of the famine in remote places or of war or trouble or change; they are the means by which this great earth and its peoples have become one to one another, the means by which the news of discovery or honor and the stories and songs of today travel and resound throughout the world. But they are also the means by which the true human community, the man knowing man, the neighbor understanding neighbor, the schoolboy learning a poem, the women dancing, the individual curiosity, the individual sense of beauty are being blown dry and issueless, the means by which the passivity of the disengaged spectator presents to the man of art and science the bleak face of unhumanity.

For the truth is that this is indeed, inevitably and increasingly, an open and, inevitably and increasingly, an eclectic world. We know too much for one man to know much, we live too variously to live as one. Our histories and traditions—the very means of interpreting life—are both bonds and barriers among us. Our knowledge separates as well as it unites; our orders disintegrate as well as bind; our art brings us together and sets us apart. The artist's loneliness, the scholar despairing because no one will any longer trouble to learn what he can teach, the narrowness of the scientist—these are unnatural insignia in this great time of change.

For what is asked of us is not easy. The openness of this world derives its character from the irreversibility of learning; what is once learned is part of human life. We cannot close our minds to discovery; we cannot stop our ears so that the voices of far-off and strange people can no longer reach them. The great cultures of the East cannot be walled off from ours by impassable seas and defects of understanding based on ignorance and unfamiliarity. Neither our integrity as men of learning nor our humanity allows that. In this open world, what is there, any man may try to learn.

This is no new problem. There has always been more to know than one man could know; there have always been modes of feeling that could not move the same heart; there have always been deeply held beliefs that could not be composed into a synthetic union. Yet never before today have the diversity, the complexity, the richness so clearly defied hierarchical order and simplification; never before have we had to understand the complementary, mutually not compatible ways of life and recognize choice between them as the only course of freedom. Never before today has the integrity of the intimate, the detailed, the true art, the integrity of craftsmanship and the preservation of the familiar, of the humorous and the beautiful stood in more massive contrast to the vastness of life, the greatness of the globe, the otherness of people, the otherness of ways, and the all-encompassing dark.

This is a world in which each of us, knowing his limitations, knowing the evils of superficiality and the terrors of fatigue, will have to cling to what is close to him, to what he knows, to what he can do, to his friends and his tradition and his love, lest he be dissolved in a universal confusion and know nothing and love nothing. It is at the same time a world in which none of us can find hieratic prescription or general sanction for any ignorance, any insensitivity, any indifference. When a friend tells us of a new discovery we may not understand, we may not be able to listen without jeopardizing the work that is ours and closer to us; but we cannot find in a book or canon—and we should not seek—grounds for hallowing our ignorance. If a man tells us that he sees differently than we, or that he finds beautiful what we find ugly, we may have to leave the room, from fatigue or trouble; but that is our weakness and our default. If we must live with a perpetual sense that the world and the men in it are greater than we and too much for us, let it be the measure of our virtue that we know this and seek no comfort. Above all, let us not proclaim that the limits of our powers correspond to some special wisdom in our choice of life, of learning, or of beauty.

This balance, this perpetual, precarious, impossible balance between the infinitely open and the intimate, this time—our twentieth century—has been long in coming; but it has come. It is, I think, for us and our children, our only way.

This is for all men. For the artist and for the scientist there is a special problem and a special hope, for in their extraordinarily different ways, in their lives that have increasingly divergent character, there is still a sensed bond, a sensed analogy. Both the man of science and the man of art live always at the edge of mystery, surrounded by it; both always, as the measure of their creation, have had to do with the harmonization of what is new with what is familiar, with the balance between novelty and synthesis, with the struggle to make partial order in total chaos. They can, in their work and in their lives, help themselves, help one another, and help all men. They can make the paths that connect the villages of arts and sciences with each other and with the world at large the multiple, varied, precious bonds of a true and world-wide community.

This cannot be an easy life. We shall have a rugged time of it to keep our minds open and to keep them deep, to keep our sense of beauty and our ability to make it, and our occasional ability to see it in places remote and strange and unfamiliar; we shall have a rugged time of it, all of us, in keeping these gardens in our villages, in keeping open the manifold, intricate, casual paths, to keep these flourishing in a great, open, windy world; but this, as I see it, is the condition of man; and in this condition we can help, because we can love, one another.

ABOUT THE AUTHOR

J. ROBERT OPPENHEIMER *has been director of the Institute for Advanced Study at Princeton, New Jersey, since 1947. He is a physicist trained at Harvard, Cambridge and Göttingen who was for eighteen years Professor of Physics at the University of California and at the California Institute of Technology. Between 1943 and 1945 he was director of the laboratory at Los Alamos in New Mexico, where the first atomic bombs were made. From 1945 through 1953 he served in many advisory positions to the Atomic Energy Commission, the White House, and the Departments of State and Defense; in the spring of 1954, in a much publicized proceeding, he was denied security clearance. He is the author of* Science and the Common Understanding, *published by Simon and Schuster in 1954.*